HANDLE WITH CARE

RICHARD CAMERON

Resource Material
Cecily O'Neill

Series Consultant
Cecily O'Neill

COLLINS
EDUCATIONAL

Collins Educational, 8 Grafton Street, London W1X 3LA
© Playscript, Richard Cameron, end-material Cecily O'Neill
First published 1988

ISBN 0 00 330238 5

Cover design by the Pinpoint Design Co.

Photographs
Front cover Sally & Richard Greenhill, p. 77 John Sturrock/Network, p.
78 The National Children's Home, pp. 80, 83 and 88 Universal
Pictorial Press, p. 90 Fortean Picture Library.

Typesetting by Northern Phototypesetting Company, Bolton
Printed and bound in Great Britain by Scotprint Ltd, Musselburgh

CONTENTS

PLAYSCRIPT OF *HANDLE WITH CARE*   1

STAGING THE PLAY   73

BACKGROUND TO THE PLAY   75

WORKING ON AND AROUND THE SCRIPT   84

THE SUPERNATURAL   89

THE CHARACTERS

TERRY — Fourteen. He is hyperactive and desperate for friendship. He is the butt of many jokes.

JAY — Sixteen. The eldest in the home. He is brooding and sometimes aggressive. Despite all his faults he somehow draws people to him.

BARRY — Eleven. A thin boy, with wild frightened eyes. He wears a hearing aid and lives within his own world. He has bruises on his arms and face.

FRANKIE — Fourteen. He idolises Jay.

MARGERY — Thirteen, but she looks much younger. Lonely and lost.

BRENDA — Fifteen. Sullen and scheming. She is strong willed but somehow vulnerable.

CAROL — Fourteen. Part of a large family no longer together. Helps out around the home.

LIZ — House parent in charge. She is a little over thirty, competent, dedicated. She is unmarried but engaged.

HOWARD — House parent, assistant to Liz. He is in his late twenties. He enjoys his job but is not too good at all the administration.

MOTHER — Margery's mother. She is in her early thirties but looks much older despite all the make up she uses. Neurotic, has drifted through a number of affairs.

SOCIAL WORKER — Mid thirties. Efficient, smartly dressed.

A HOUSE NOT RIGHT IN THE HEAD

SCENE 1

The main room of 'Sunflowers', a home for children in care.
Barry *is sitting in 'his' chair, listening to a transistor*
radio. **Liz** *is kneeling beside him trying to mend his deaf*
aid. **Terry** *is sprawled on the floor reading a comic.*
Margery *is sitting at a table, embroidering a piece of*
material. From somewhere else in the house we can hear a
Christmas carol being sung. **Carol** *enters from the hall*
with a plastic watering can and starts to water the solitary
plant in a pot on the table. It is a peaceful scene, the
beginning of another quiet day. The music stops.

TERRY *to Liz*   I like it here, Miss.

LIZ   That's nice, Terry.

TERRY   I like you, too.

LIZ   Thank you.

TERRY   You're alright, you are, you're funny.

LIZ   Oh?

TERRY   Yes. I'm going to buy you something, 'cause
you're my friend.

LIZ   I don't think you ought to spend your pocket money
on me.

TERRY   I'll make you something, then, Miss. I'm clever
at making things. I've made a rocket. Will we be getting
beans today?

LIZ   What?

TERRY   If we get beans can you save me the cans and
then I can make another rocket?

LIZ   That would be good.

TERRY   It wouldn't get broke would it? If I made one? Would you keep it safe?

LIZ   Yes.

TERRY   I can make rocket fuel as well. I've got a chemistry set. I've invented some plastic and some perfume. I could make you some of my perfume. You can't ask me what's in it, though, 'cause it's a secret recipe.

Frankie enters from the hall.

FRANKIE   *to Terry*   He's doing your scene now.

TERRY   Me?   *running off*   Ebenezer Scroooooge.

*He pauses by **Barry** to give him a ghostly manic laugh which has no effect at all and rushes out.*

FRANKIE   I've got a splinter. I got it off that scenery. There's only me doing anything. Everyone else is just messing about.   *to **Carol***   Look at that, it goes right in. Have you got a pin?

MARGERY   Here, use my needle.

LIZ   I'll do it.   *she takes the needle*   Thanks, Margery.   *takes Frankie's hand*   Now, where is it? Is that it?

FRANKIE   Yea.   *pause*   The doctor's been to see Brenda, hasn't he? I saw his car. What's wrong with her?

LIZ   She's not been sleeping properly.

FRANKIE   She's seen a ghost, hasn't she?

LIZ   Don't be silly.

FRANKIE   She has. Last night. She said so.

LIZ   She said so?

FRANKIE   Well, not her, no, but that's what they're saying.

LIZ   Who's they?

FRANKIE   Everybody. Everybody knows. Oh!

LIZ   Keep still, I've nearly got it out.

FRANKIE   She says she has seen a ghost. Honest.

Jay enters through the French windows.

2

FRANKIE   Ask Jay.

Liz does not respond. **Jay** *picks up* **Margery's** *piece of material. She is anxious as he examines it.*

LIZ   There. You need a magnifying glass to see it.

Liz turns to give **Margery** *her needle back. Jay drops the material back on the table.*

LIZ   *to* **Jay**   Now what do you want?

JAY   I live here, don't I?

LIZ   to **Margery**   Thanks. How's it coming?

MARGERY   I've nearly finished it.

LIZ   It's lovely.   *to* **Carol**   It's nice, isn't it, Carol?

CAROL   What is it?

MARGERY   It's a special cloth I've made for holding kettles and teapots. I've made it all by myself. It's for my mother. Look, I've stitched her name on it. She'll be here in a minute. She's coming to see me. She's coming to see me today. It's her birthday. Do you think she'll like it?

CAROL   It's alright.

MARGERY   Have you ever made anything for your mum?

CAROL   Which one?

MARGERY   It's taken me ages to make it. I'll have to wrap it up soon.

Howard appears in the doorway.

HOWARD   I thought you were involved in this play, Frankie?

FRANKIE   No.

HOWARD   Yes you are.

FRANKIE   No I'm not. I'm not in it, am I?

HOWARD   I know, but you're working backstage, aren't you?

FRANKIE   I know that.

HOWARD   Well then.   *to* **Jay**   I want you.

JAY   I'm not going to be in it.

HOWARD   I'm not on about the play.

LIZ   What's wrong?

HOWARD   *to Jay*   Have you been in the store cupboard?

JAY   No.

HOWARD   *to Liz*   Somebody's been in there.

Terry runs in.

TERRY   Howard, can you come a minute? The tape recorder's stopped working.

LIZ   *to Howard*   Anything missing?

CAROL   *pointing to Jay*   He was in the store cupboard this morning.

JAY   Get lost.

CAROL   He was. I saw him.

HOWARD   Were you?

TERRY   It's got stuck and all the tape's going curly wurly.

HOWARD   In a minute, Terry. Jay?

JAY   She's lying.

TERRY   Has he been bad?

HOWARD   While I'm spending my time sorting this play out this is what you're doing? There's stuff thrown all over the place and that spray can snow all over the back of the door.

TERRY   He's naughty, isn't he?

HOWARD   Terry, go through, will you?

TERRY   Can I do some more sound effects?

HOWARD   Just leave it.

Jay starts to walk out. He pauses in passing Carol.

JAY   *to Carol*   I'll get you for this.

HOWARD   Where do you think you're going?

JAY   Nowhere.

HOWARD   You can't just walk away from things.

JAY   I'll stay here, then.

Carol is worried. Terry moves across to Barry.

TERRY *to Barry* I don't need a tape recorder anyway.

He begins to make his own sound effects — creaking doors, wind howling, an owl . . . meanwhile—

LIZ *to Jay* You'd better go and try to get it off the door.

JAY No.

HOWARD Yes.

JAY Not me. Not when I didn't do it, I won't. I haven't been near the store cupboard.

HOWARD Well somebody has!

JAY Yea, well it weren't BLOODY ME!

A shocked pause for a moment, then—

TERRY It might have been the ghost.

HOWARD What?

TERRY It might have been a ghost messing it all up. They do sometimes when they get mad. They throw things about. Flying saucers. And cups.

CAROL It might have been somebody else.

HOWARD What?

CAROL It could have been somebody else. I didn't see him properly. *moving off* I'll clean it up, I don't mind.

She is making for the door quickly. Terry suddenly chases and stops her.

TERRY Hey! You can't.

CAROL Why not?

TERRY 'Cause it'll be all melted! Ha!

Carol goes out.

HOWARD Jay, will you come through a minute, help me sort out this tape?

TERRY What about me?

HOWARD Jay?

JAY If you say so.

TERRY What am I going to do?

HOWARD   Have a rest!   *to Liz*   I wouldn't mind a coffee.

No response from Liz. Howard goes out with Jay. Liz tidies up Terry's nest of comics.

TERRY   *at the door, shouting out*   I'VE HAD A REST!   *he comes back in*   I don't think he likes me. Do you think he likes me, Miss? I'm not going to buy him anything.

He rushes back to the door, shouting.

TERRY   I'm going to make him some poison!

He comes back in.

TERRY   It could have been a ghost. I know somebody who's seen one. I nearly did but I wasn't with them when they saw it.

Nobody is listening. Liz is showing Margery how to finish her stitches, Barry listens to the radio.

TERRY   If it was a ghost it would be all cold in the cupboard. They do make the temperature go cold, I read it.   *to Barry, very close*   Hey, that's why it was snowing. Ha ha! I could make a ghost meter, I've got some red wire.

Margery, leaving Liz to her sewing has moved across to the window. She looks out, turns to Terry.

MARGERY   Do you know what time it is?

TERRY   *to Margery*   I'd draw it all out on paper first. A circuit diagram.

MARGERY   Excuse me.

TERRY   Do you believe in ghosts?

MARGERY   I don't know.

TERRY   I do.

LIZ   It's half eleven. Your Mum won't be here till after dinner.

MARGERY   Oh.

TERRY   *to Liz*   Do you believe in them, Miss?

LIZ   No.

6

TERRY   I do. We had one in our house. I had a pet budgie and my Dad had to kill it because it had a growth under its chin like a bit of brain but he couldn't do it so I did it. I put it in a plastic bag and held it over the gas ring and gassed it. I put it in a big matchbox with some daisies and buried it in our back yard and for ages after we kept hearing it chirping and bashing its bell to bits but when we went in the kitchen it weren't there and anyway we'd sold the cage.

Pause.

MARGERY   You shouldn't kill animals.

TERRY   I know.   *pause*   I killed some worms once.

LIZ   Alright.

TERRY   I used to do experiments on them with my chemistry set.

LIZ   Terry!

TERRY   I didn't mean to kill them. I forgot to take them out of the solution when I went for my tea.

LIZ   Terry!

TERRY   They'd gone all soggy when I got back.

LIZ   Will you shut up?

TERRY   Don't you like worms?

LIZ   No.

TERRY   There's some big juicy ones at the bottom of the garden. I'm off to get one.

LIZ   No, Terry.

TERRY   I won't hurt it.

LIZ   No!

TERRY   You said you were my friend, but you're not really, are you?

He flops down, grabs a comic from the neat pile and flips noisily through the pages.

LIZ   Of course I am your friend.   *to **Margery***
Come on, let's go in the garden, Margery.

MARGERY   There aren't any flowers.

LIZ   No. The trees look nice, though.

MARGERY   Are we going to grow flowers.

LIZ   Mmm. Next year. Sunflowers.

MARGERY   What are they?

LIZ   Great big yellow flowers. They grow ever so high, bigger than you.

MARGERY   I think I like them.

Margery takes her cloth and goes out into the garden with Liz. Barry is still listening to the radio. Terry chooses another comic, making a mess of the pile. He chuckles to himself as he reads the jokes. From somewhere else in the house hammering begins. Carol enters and makes her way over to the French windows.

TERRY   It's funny this. Hey, listen to this. What do you call a – no – what – wait a minute   *she is almost gone*   What's white on the outside and green in the middle?

CAROL   *going into the garden, bored*   A frog sandwich.

TERRY   *as if hearing the punch line for the first time*   A frog sandwich. Ha ha!

Terry looks at the comic some more, chuckling, laughing, then suddenly throws it away, bored. He listens to the hammering.

TERRY   Knock knock. Who's there? You. You who? Yoooohoooo. Ha ha. That's silly. Knock knock. Who's there? Me. Oh, you'd better come in, then.

*He moves across to **Barry**. Whispering loudly in his ear—*

TERRY   Knock knock.   *silence*   Knock knock.

Jay and Frankie enter, unseen by Terry. Barry is looking at Terry with frightened eyes.

TERRY   Come on, you're supposed to say, 'Who's there?'

JAY   Who's there?

TERRY   Willy.

He laughs and then suddenly realises there is someone else in the room.

8

TERRY Eh?

FRANKIE Willy who?

TERRY That's a rude word, that, my Dad told me.

JAY Hey! *he commands silence, listens to the knocks* It's a spirit calling, Terry, trying to get through from the other side.

TERRY It's not, then, it's Howard building scenery. *pause* Aren't you helping any more?

Jay and Frankie sit. Jay takes out some chewing gum, offers Frankie a piece.

TERRY Do you know any rude words?

JAY Yea.

TERRY What?

Jay crooks his finger and beckons Terry close. He whispers in his ear.

JAY Aaaaah. Ha ha. Hooo. *pause* What does that mean?

Jay and Frankie exchange a look. Bored. The hammering stops.

TERRY Don't you like it here?

JAY Yea.

FRANKIE Yea, we really love it here.

TERRY I do as well.

Pause. Jay blows a bubble.

TERRY Can I have a piece of chewy, please?

JAY Oh, sorry. Sure, course you can, Terry. *pause* You won't swallow it will you?

Terry puts the gum cautiously into his mouth.

TERRY No.

JAY It'll wrap around your insides and strangle your intestines if you do. *to **Frankie**, with a wink* Won't it?

FRANKIE Yes.

TERRY It won't.

JAY It will. Honest.

TERRY *unsure* It won't.

JAY Knew somebody who died of it. Terrible agonizing death. I was with him right up until the end. It formed a big bubble inside him. He just got bigger and bigger. I was with him in the hospital. Do you know what his last words to me were, Terry?

TERRY *enthralled* No, what?

JAY 'Jay', he said, 'Jay, as you travel down life's highway remember these words. . . .' Well, he didn't say it like that, 'cause he could hardly talk. It was sort of . . . *in a croaky voice* 'As you travel down life's highway, remember these words. Always put your bubbly on the bedpost overnight.'

Terry is totally absorbed. Frankie is trying hard to keep a straight face.

JAY 'Yes, George,' I said, 'go on, is that it?' Suddenly his eyes glazed. I called the nurse and she prepared an injection. As soon as she stuck it in him he went BANG!

Terry nearly swallows his gum.

JAY All over the world I've always remembered what he said to me. Of course, it's got a deep meaning, you know. It's not just about chewing gum. It's about life.

TERRY *not seeing* I see.

JAY Life and death. It helps explain some of the mystery. Why we're here, what's our purpose. Why we live, why we die. Where we go after.

TERRY We go to Heaven.

JAY Or Hell.

TERRY Yes.

JAY Or fertiliser. That's what I want. *seriously* I want them to throw my ashes in the garden and grow flowers with me. *pause, then, to **Frankie** –* Do you believe in reincarnation?

TERRY What do you want to be a carnation for?

JAY No, I'm not talking about flowers. I'm not talking about flowers now, am I? I'm talking about when we die, coming back as someone or something else.

TERRY And you want to come back as a carnation?

JAY No. I mean, you might come back as a scientist.

TERRY I am a scientist.

JAY Alright then, you might come back as a . . . as a . . .

TERRY Worm?

JAY Eh?

TERRY I don't want to come back as one of them. I might get chopped up.

JAY Well what do you want to come back as?

TERRY Einstein.

JAY No. No you can't come back as him, Terry, he's already been and gone.

TERRY Oh. Can't you do that?

JAY No, Terry.

TERRY That's what my Dad used to call me, Einstein.

JAY I bet he used to call you a few other things as well, eh, Terry?

Jay and Frankie begin to laugh. Terry joins in. They turn it into a false, loud laugh and then suddenly stop, looking deadly serious, leaving Terry laughing alone. His laughter fades to serious silence.

JAY Don't forget. 'Always put your bubbly . . .' It's very profound that, isn't it Frankie?

TERRY *taking out the gum* I think I've found it. I hope I haven't swallowed any. I might have swallowed a bit!

FRANKIE Oh no, Terry!

JAY Oh no.

TERRY Oh no, I might die!

JAY Tell you what, my bit's about as chewed as yours. *takes gum out* We'll weigh them. If yours is lighter than mine we'll know you've swallowed some. Here.

Jay *gives him his gum.* ***Terry*** *tries to balance the two pieces in his outstretched arms.*

TERRY Oh, I can't tell. I don't know. You do it Jay!

JAY Look, I'll tell you what, go and ask if you can use the scales to weigh them on. Go on!

TERRY Shall I?

FRANKIE You'll have to.

JAY You've got to find out, haven't you?

TERRY *running out* Oooooh!

Jay *and* ***Frankie*** *collapse with laughter.*

FRANKIE He believed it. He believes anything you tell him.

JAY I'm his friend, aren't I?

FRANKIE Reincarnation.

JAY Do you believe in it?

FRANKIE No.

JAY Do you believe there's something else – a spirit world?

FRANKIE No. *gets up* Come on, let's go out.

JAY Tell you what, Frankie, when I die, I'll come back to you, just to prove there's a hereafter. I'll come back and give you a sign. I'll give you a knock. Two knocks. *taps twice.*

They go out through the French windows into the garden leaving ***Barry*** *alone. He begins to sing softly to himself.*

BARRY *sings* Brown girl in the ring, tra la la la la
Brown girl in the ring, tra la la la la la la . . .

Brenda *enters. She is very pale, almost ghost like, in a long night dress and dressing gown. She moves across the room.* ***Barry*** *senses her, stops singing, then avoiding her eyes, walks out into the garden.* ***Brenda*** *moves across to the French windows and looks out into the garden. After a while she turns, walks into the centre of the room and waits.* ***Liz*** *enters from the garden. Stops. Waits.* ***Brenda*** *turns to her.*

BRENDA It's cold upstairs.

LIZ   Get in bed, then.

BRENDA   No.

LIZ   Brenda, if you're ill, you're upstairs.

BRENDA   Please, Liz, let me stay down here.

LIZ   No.

BRENDA   Why are you keeping me away from everybody else?

LIZ   Come on.

BRENDA   Can I have a drink?

LIZ   I'll be bringing your lunch up in a minute.

BRENDA   Stay with me, then.

LIZ   I'm too busy.

BRENDA   I don't want to be on my own!   *pause. Liz goes to her*   I had another bad dream. I'm sorry. I don't want it to be like this.

Pause.

LIZ   This person you see – is it someone you know?

BRENDA   Yes. I can't remember what my mother looked like but I know it's her. She just looks at me.

LIZ   It's just a dream, Brenda, it's just a dream.

BRENDA   Yes.

LIZ   That's all it is. And a dream can't hurt you so there's no need to be frightened.

BRENDA   I can't get rid of it, can I?

LIZ   Don't keep thinking about it.

BRENDA   I'm trying to, aren't I? You asked me about her.

LIZ   OK.   *moves away*

BRENDA   Wait. Look. Can't I just talk about it?

LIZ   I gather you already have.

BRENDA   What?

LIZ   What have you been telling people?

BRENDA   Nothing. Oh, forget it, then. I won't bother. I should have –

LIZ   I don't want you frightening other people, telling them it was a ghost.

BRENDA   I never said that.

LIZ   Really?

BRENDA   I never said it was a ghost.

LIZ   OK.

BRENDA   Why don't you believe me? Why don't you ever listen to me?

Terry runs in.

TERRY   I've got them mixed up now, I don't know which is my bit! *running out into the garden*   Jay!

LIZ   I'm listening.

BRENDA   I've not thought about my Mum for years. I was only little when she died. My Grandma's always been my Mum. We had a family once but then my Dad left us and my Mum went funny. She used to get me to cry with her. And then she wasn't there any more. Now I've started thinking about her again and she won't go away. I think of anything to keep her out. I count, I do my times tables, anything, but she just gets back in.

Howard enters.

HOWARD   Dinner.

Brenda jumps up.

LIZ   Brenda!

BRENDA   No!

*She rushes out past **Howard**.*

HOWARD   Doesn't she like fish?   *pause*   Sorry. Sorry, Liz.

LIZ   It's OK.

Howard walks over to the window.

LIZ   How's the play coming?

HOWARD   Don't ask.   *shouting into the garden*   Dinner!   *to **Liz***   Hard work. I'm not getting much help.

LIZ What about Frankie?

HOWARD He's spent six weeks making a lamp post. Now he's given up on it.

LIZ He's shown it to me. I think it's good.

HOWARD Yea, but he thinks that's it now. Any graft and they all disappear.

They begin to move through into the hall.

LIZ We've got people here this afternoon, don't forget.

HOWARD Yes.

LIZ Are you rehearsing after tea?

*They are gone. **Margery** and **Carol** come in from the garden. **Margery** has a few twigs. She puts them on the table. They go through. **Barry** drifts in and through. **Jay** and **Frankie** come in.*

FRANKIE What am I going to do?

JAY I dunno. It would help if I knew who you were on about.

FRANKIE I can't tell you, Jay.

JAY Look, if you fancy someone, why can't you tell me who she is?

FRANKIE I can't.

JAY I don't know what's the matter with you, Frankie, it must be love. She must be really ugly if you're frightened to tell me who she is. Has she got a glass eye?

FRANKIE No.

JAY Wooden leg?

FRANKIE No, she's nice. What am I going to do?

JAY Faint heart never won fair maiden. Or in your case, Frankie Binns never wins glass-eyed girl unless he looks her straight in her good 'un.

***Terry** comes in from the garden.*

JAY If you think there's a chance make a move. Women can't stand shy men. Can they, Terry?

TERRY Eh?

JAY You're not shy with girls, are you?

15

TERRY No.

JAY I've been giving him lessons. Show Frankie your macho man.

TERRY No.

JAY What about Margery, eh, Terry? I told him, be dominating, be masterful. I don't know what he said but she daren't come out of her room for two days.

TERRY Jay, you know this afternoon, can I have one of your cigarettes? You said I could. Do you swallow the smoke?

JAY Yes. *pause* What you do, Terry, is you suck as hard as you can. Then you put these fingers in your ears and these two little fingers up your nose. *demonstrates* Oh, and if you can manage it, you squeeze your arse cheeks together as tight as you can – till you're an expert and then you don't have to bother with all that.

He moves to the door with **Frankie**. *Stops.* **Terry** *is trying to figure it all out.*

JAY Well you've got to block up all the holes somehow, haven't you?

He goes through into the hall with **Frankie**.

TERRY *not seeing* I see. *running after them* You're an expert, aren't you, Jay? You'll let me smoke one, then?

SCENE 2

The main room, afternoon. **Margery** *is at the table, putting sticky tape around her wrapped present.* **Frankie** *is by the window, looking out.* **Carol** *is sat on the sofa, leafing through a magazine.* **Liz** *enters.*

LIZ   Carol, come on! Frankie, I've just had a call from your brother.

FRANKIE   Eddie?

LIZ   Yes. He can't make it. Not this afternoon.

FRANKIE   He was taking me out on his bike.

LIZ   Yes. He's sorry. One of his mates is ill and he's looking after him.

FRANKIE   I bet.

LIZ   Come on, don't be like that.

FRANKIE   Like what? I'm not bothered. It's gonna rain anyway.

LIZ   I suggested if he could get away later for an hour we wouldn't mind if he came round tonight.

FRANKIE   What did he say?

LIZ   He said he would try. OK?

FRANKIE   Sure.

LIZ   Carol, please.

CAROL   No. I've told you, I'm not seeing them.

LIZ   Why not? They're nice people. They care about you. What about Jane and Robert, you like them, don't you?

CAROL   They don't like me.

LIZ   Yes they do. They want you to live with them, don't they? The whole family likes you.

CAROL   Well I don't like them. I'm staying here.

LIZ   They'll be taking you up to the park again I expect, for the afternoon. You liked it last time – the lake, and the ducks.

CAROL   I shoot them.

LIZ   What?

CAROL   I've shot loads. Me and my brother with his air gun.

LIZ   Don't lie.

CAROL   I'm not going up the park with them. They're all snobs.

LIZ   What do you want?

CAROL   I don't want another family. If I can't have the one I've got, I'll do without. I'll stay here.

LIZ   Carol, they'll be here in a minute.

CAROL   Oh God. *getting up and moving out*   I suppose I'll have to put my dress on. A pity it's not pretty pink with ribbons. They'd all want me then, wouldn't they? It's like choosing a doll.

*She goes through into the hall, followed by **Liz**.*

HOWARD   *from the garden*   Get in the house, now! Both of you!

*Jay and **Terry** enter from the garden. **Terry** is walking oddly. He has his fingers up his nose and in his ears. **Howard** follows them in.*

HOWARD   You can't be left alone for five minutes, can you? Well? What have you got to say for yourselves? Jay?

Jay   Nothing. He asked me if I wanted a fag, that's all. He had a fag lit and he gave it to me but I said I didn't want it. I was just stubbing it out when you came round the corner.

HOWARD   You mean you stubbed it out when you saw me. Terry?

18

TERRY Mmm?

HOWARD Do you mind telling me why you have your fingers in your ears?

*Jay manages to slip his packet of cigarettes to **Frankie**.*

TERRY Mmm?

HOWARD Take your fingers out of your ears!

He does so, but pinches his nose.

HOWARD What are you playing at?

Terry begins to flap his free arm about to help him explain.

TERRY Mmm mmmmmm mmm mm mmmmmm. . . .

HOWARD Talk properly!

*Jay gives **Terry** a sharp dig in the ribs. He exhales sharply and begins breathing heavily. Seeing no smoke he is curious and exhales several short sharp breaths.*

TERRY It's gone. It's all gone. *looks between his legs* Where's it all gone?

HOWARD Terry, I thought you didn't smoke?

TERRY I don't. Well, I do now.

HOWARD Did he give it to you?

TERRY Yes. He's my friend.

JAY Thanks.

TERRY No, thank you. It was alright, that.

HOWARD I don't want you doing that any more. *to Jay* I'll have the packet please.

*Jay holds up his arms to be frisked. **Howard** frisks him and finds a solitary stubbed cigarette in his shirt pocket. He crumples it and gives it to **Jay**.*

HOWARD Dustbin.

JAY *moving through into the hall* I was giving up anyway.

HOWARD *to Terry* You go and have a lie down, you look green.

TERRY I'm alright. I don't need a lie down. You're always wanting me to have a rest. It's like the hospital in here!

19

HOWARD   I'm just telling you to have a lie down, that's all.

Terry drops to the floor, lies flat on his back.

HOWARD   Not here. Get up!

TERRY   I'm lying down, aren't I?

Howard tries to get him up. Terry begins chuckling and laughing.

TERRY   That tickles.

HOWARD   Come on, Terry.

Margery's mother appears in the doorway.

HOWARD   Oh, hello, there. We've been waiting for you, haven't we, Margery?

Margery rushes to her mother, throws her arms around her. Terry is still giggling.

MOTHER   Don't do that, dear, you'll get wet. My coat's a bit wet.

HOWARD   *to Terry*   Get up!

Terry suddenly stops and jumps to attention.

MOTHER   And how is Howard?

HOWARD   Fine, thanks.

MOTHER   Lovely weather.

HOWARD   Yes,

MARGERY   Happy birthday, Mummy.

MOTHER   *to Howard*   They always have to remind you you're getting older, don't they?

HOWARD   Yes. Er . . . Frankie, is there anybody still outside?

FRANKIE   Barry.

HOWARD   Fetch him in for me, will you?

Frankie goes into the garden. Howard takes Terry out.

HOWARD   Excuse us.

They are gone.

20

MARGERY *releasing her mother* Wait there. I've got you a present.

She goes to the table.

MOTHER Do you like this? *shows bangle* Your uncle Joe bought me this. He's here now, outside. He brought me. Doesn't like to intrude.

MARGERY Yes, it's lovely. Here. I made it.

MOTHER Made?

MARGERY Yes.

MOTHER *struggling to open it* You open it for me, love, I'll break my nails.

Margery opens it for her.

MARGERY Happy birthday, Mummy.

MOTHER Oh, thanks love. You shouldn't have. *examines it* Oh, Margery, what did you have to put 'mother' on it for? Makes me feel ancient, like a Grandma. It's made me go all cold.

MARGERY Don't you like it?

MOTHER Yes, it's lovely, love. What is it?

MARGERY It's a teapot holder.

MOTHER I don't drink tea.

MARGERY Well it's for anything hot.

MOTHER It's lovely. Very practical. Thanks, love. You could put a vase of flowers on it. *puts it on the table* Well. Are you settled in all right now?

MARGERY I don't like it here, I want to come home.

Frankie enters from the garden.

MARGERY Let me come home, Mummy.

MOTHER Now give over, don't start all that.

MARGERY Please.

MOTHER Now stop it or I'm going. I haven't come here for this. Pull yourself together, you're not a baby, are you?

MARGERY Yes, I am! You never let me be a baby. I always had to be grown up.

21

MOTHER   I'm going.

MARGERY   Oh, no. Please. Don't go.

MOTHER   Well shut up, then!

*An embarrassed pause. **Frankie** is watching. **Mother** meets his eyes, smiles vaguely. **Margery** sobs.*

MOTHER   It's a nice place, this.

***Barry** comes in from the garden. He is carrying a dirty old doll as well as his radio.*

FRANKIE   Don't bring it in here. He won't chuck it away, it's full of earwigs.

***Barry** holds it out for **Margery**.*

MARGERY   For me?

FRANKIE   *trying to steer him out*   Come on.

MARGERY   *taking the doll*   Thanks, Barry.

***Frankie** and **Barry** go through.*

MOTHER   You don't know what's crawling about inside that. Put it outside.

***Margery** reluctantly does so.*

MOTHER   Dolls at your age. You get worse. Mind you, your father always was a bit of a nance.

***Margery** looks out into the garden.*

MOTHER   Do you want me to come and see you again next week?

MARGERY   Don't go!

MOTHER   I've got to. Uncle Joe's hired a car for the day. You've got to make good use of it when it costs that much.

MARGERY   It's raining.

MOTHER   We've arranged to go out with some friends if you must know, being as it's my birthday. I can do that, can't I?

MARGERY   Yes, I want you to have a nice birthday. I'm sorry I'm spoiling it for you.

22

MOTHER   You're not. I wouldn't be here if I didn't want to come and see you.   *pause*   Well, then, we'll be seeing you again next week, if Joe can get another car. It was good of him to bring me, you know.

MARGERY   Yes. Thank him for me.

MOTHER   Ta ta, then.

She puts her face down for a kiss. **Margery** *tries to hold on to her.*

MOTHER   Mind my hair.

Margery relaxes her hold.

MOTHER   You be a good girl and we'll see you again next weekend. Ta ra.

MARGERY   *following her to the door*   Goodbye, Mummy.

Mother is gone. **Margery** *stands in the doorway for a while then comes back into the room. She sees the teapot holder, grabs it, rushes to the door, then back to the window. She waves and a car horn toots in response.* **Margery** *remains looking out for a moment before turning back into the room, crying. She tries to wipe away the tears with the present. After a while* **Liz** *enters.*

LIZ   Hello, Margery, still waiting?

MARGERY   No, she's just been.

LIZ   Oh? Did you forget to give her your present after all that?

MARGERY   Yes.

LIZ   I don't know.

MARGERY   Yes, I forgot.

LIZ   Never mind, you can give it to her next time. It's lovely, such a lot of work.

MARGERY   Do you want it?

LIZ   Of course not.   *pause*   Are you going into the games room?   **Margery** *shakes her head*   Watch television? I'll tell you what, I know what you'd like to do, play in the dolls' house, you like that. You play in there for a while, yes?

23

MARGERY   No.

LIZ   But I thought you liked the dolls' house?

MARGERY   It's for babies.

LIZ   No. It's for pretending. We all like to pretend sometimes. Even me.

MARGERY   You're a woman, you should act like one.

LIZ   Should I?

MARGERY   Yes.

LIZ   And when you're grown up you're not supposed to pretend?

MARGERY   No.

LIZ   I see.   *pause*   That would make life very boring. Daydreams help.

MARGERY   There isn't a Father Christmas.

LIZ   I believe there is.

MARGERY   No fairies at the bottom of the garden, either.

LIZ   Not today, they're sheltering from the rain.

MARGERY   You're stupid.

LIZ   Am I?

MARGERY   Yes. There isn't anything else. There's nothing else. You live in nursery rhymes, fairy stories, Disneyland.

LIZ   Sometimes.

MARGERY   Huh.

LIZ   And you never do?

Pause.

MARGERY   Do you believe in God?

LIZ   Of course.

MARGERY   Heaven and hell?

LIZ   Well –

MARGERY   Do you think there's a heaven?

LIZ   Hey, one at a time. So many questions.

MARGERY   I suppose you believe in ghosts, like Brenda.

24

LIZ No. *pause* Well, if you're not going to play with the dolls' house we'd better give it away to somewhere where the children will use it. *moves away*

MARGERY No, don't send it away.

LIZ There's no point in keeping it since you're so determined to be grown up, not playing silly games.

MARGERY I never was allowed any dolls.

LIZ No?

MARGERY I'd never seen a dolls' house before.

LIZ There's nothing wrong in catching up on what you've missed.

MARGERY People will think I'm silly.

LIZ I won't.

MARGERY I'll just have a look at it, then.

*As they move to the door, **Frankie** enters.*

LIZ Hello, Frankie.

FRANKIE I'm fed up with that lot, they're getting on my nerves.

LIZ I'll leave you to your peace and quiet, then.

FRANKIE No, don't go. I . . . I wanted to talk to you.

LIZ Oh?

Margery goes out.

FRANKIE Has Jay said anything to you?

LIZ No. What about?

FRANKIE Me.

LIZ Should he have?

FRANKIE No.

LIZ What's wrong?

FRANKIE You're getting married, aren't you?

LIZ I don't know.

FRANKIE But you're engaged?

LIZ Yes, I'm engaged.

FRANKIE Are you in love?

LIZ Frankie, what is all this?

25

FRANKIE   What's he like?

LIZ   He's alright. Look –

FRANKIE   I just wanted to know if you were in love.

LIZ   Why?

FRANKIE   I . . . So I . . . so you could maybe tell me what it's like.

LIZ   I don't know.

FRANKIE   You're not in love with him?

LIZ   It means different things to different people.

FRANKIE   You are in love with him.

LIZ   What's it to you? *pause* You've found yourself a girl, haven't you?

FRANKIE   No.

LIZ   Yes you have, and you want to know if it's love.

FRANKIE   No.

LIZ   What's she like? Who is she?

FRANKIE   You don't know her.

LIZ   What's she like? Come on.

FRANKIE   *with difficulty* She's nice. She's kind. She understands me. *looks at her* She's got nice eyes.

LIZ   What's her name?

FRANKIE   Er . . .

LIZ   You don't know?

FRANKIE   Elizabeth.

LIZ   Oh well, she's bound to be nice with Elizabeth for a name, isn't she?

FRANKIE   Yes.

LIZ   Where'd you meet her?

FRANKIE   Around.

LIZ   Crafty. You'll have to bring her along sometime, let us meet her.

*Jay and **Terry** burst in.*

JAY   Frankie!

*They stop dead when they see **Liz**.*

LIZ Now what are you up to?

JAY Nothing.

LIZ Where are you going?

JAY Nowhere.

LIZ Don't go outside.

JAY We're not going outside, are we, Terry?

TERRY No.

Liz goes out.

JAY Quick! Listen, we've got a brilliant idea.

FRANKIE What?

JAY Tonight, after we've been put to bed, we're having a seance.

FRANKIE A what?

JAY A seance. You all sit in a circle, see, and put all the lights out. Put a candle in the middle, and everybody concentrates really hard on calling up a ghost. Get it? We'll call up the ghost that Brenda thinks she's seen.

FRANKIE Will we?

JAY Nah, course not!

TERRY Doh, he's a dumbo, i'nt he?

JAY We're gonna rig it, aren't we? So everybody thinks they've seen a ghost. It'll be a laugh.

Terry laughs.

FRANKIE It'll scare them.

JAY It's meant to. Look, I've got all these wires and this battery and things in my pocket all joined up. I've just tried it out in the loo. You get a real belt of a shock.

FRANKIE How?

JAY Wires go from the battery, through this train set transformer then from there down my sleeves into my hands. If I join hands I get a shock, see. All we have to do is to get everybody to join hands. As soon as one of my hands touches the person's next to me it makes a circuit – everybody gets a shock. A big blue flash will go round the ring.

FRANKIE How did you figure all that out?

JAY Great eh? My mate Einstein. He's a genius, isn't he?

FRANKIE It sounds dangerous.

JAY Nah, it'll just make 'em jump a bit. Then . . . then we have the pièce de résistance.

FRANKIE The what?

JAY Then, right on cue, Terry's gonna come through the door covered in a white sheet and give them all the ghostie effects. Eh Terry? We'll show him, then.

TERRY *demonstrating* Oooooooh Oooooooooh Oooo—

JAY That's it. Keep practising. *to **Frankie*** What do you think?

FRANKIE I think you're mad.

JAY Alright, Terry, come on, we'll do it without him. *to Frankie* Don't you let on to anybody. Right?

FRANKIE You all wired up now?

JAY Yea, I've just tried it.

FRANKIE Do it, then, let's have a look.

JAY You want to try it?

FRANKIE Yes, alright.

JAY I think you get more of a belt with just a few. The more there is, the less shock, see. They'll just get a strong tingle.

FRANKIE Let's have a go, then.

JAY Come on, Terry.

TERRY No.

JAY Come on.

TERRY No. I'll keep watch *goes to door.*

JAY Right. *holds one of **Frankie**'s hands* Are you ready?

*Jay joins both hands. Immediately they jump apart with a yell and a laugh. **Terry** forgets his watch and begins his ghostie effects as they dance about and shake their hands. **Liz** enters.*

JAY Pins and needles!

28

LIZ   What's going on?

FRANKIE   I've got cramp!

LIZ   Your tea is ready. Come on and stop messing about.

Liz goes. They decide to have another quick test. This time Jay and Frankie grab Terry and hold a hand each. He struggles. Jay makes contact.

TERRY   Aaaaah Aaaaaaah!

JAY   *checking the wiring*   It didn't work.

FRANKIE   Why? What's up with it?

JAY   A wire must have come off.

They go out.

SCENE 3

After tea, the main room. The room is empty but we can hear snatches of conversation drifting in from the games room.

VOICE *off stage* Mr Scrooge, Mr Scrooge, can you spare a penny for a poor young beggar boy?

HOWARD *off* Hold on, hold on. What are you doing?

FRANKIE *off* What?

HOWARD *off* What are you doing on stage?

FRANKIE *off* Moving the lamp post.

HOWARD *off* Look, if you've put it in the wrong place during the scene change you don't come out half way through the next scene and move it.

Laughter.

FRANKIE *off* I'm sorry.

HOWARD *off* Now what are you doing?

FRANKIE *off* Leaving it.

HOWARD *off, amid general laughter from the group* Oh no, I don't believe it. Pick it up and put it on the proper side of the stage.

FRANKIE *off* But you said not to move it!

HOWARD *off* You've stopped the scene, haven't you? We're not doing anything, we're stopped. We're waiting for you. Move it! *pause* Where are you going? Where are you going? Bring it back!

30

Frankie runs on with his lamp post, hastily followed by
Howard. *Frankie gets the sofa between them.*

HOWARD   Give me that lamp post.

FRANKIE   I made it and I can do what I want with it. I
can smash it if I want to!

HOWARD   Don't be daft, Frankie, we need it.

FRANKIE   It took me ages to make this.

*The others are wandering in now, in oddments of victorian
costume.*

HOWARD   I know, Frankie, and we're all very grateful.

FRANKIE   I asked you. Can I be in the play, I said I
wanted to be in the play or help or something. Anything.
You're not bothered, though, are you? You're not
bothered about ME! Oh, he can make the lamp post, save
me a job, and if he doesn't, no sweat, somebody else will.
WELL ALRIGHT! I'VE MADE IT! IT TOOK ME –

HOWARD   Calm down, Frankie, just–

FRANKIE   GET LOST! Just GET LOST, WILL YOU? You don't
know what it was like.

HOWARD   Yes I do.

FRANKIE   No, I don't mean how hard it was to make. I
don't mean that. I mean how much I wanted to make it –
for you – make it look good, finish it. Well I've made it,
I've finished it. I've shown you I can do it, so that's it. It
took me a long time to make but I can smash it in
seconds, smash it now and you can go and tramp around
the streets getting the stuff to make another and you
can walk out on stage and put it in the right place and
save yourself the bother of trusting some idiot like me to
do it.

HOWARD   We need the lamp post, Frankie.

FRANKIE   Yea?

HOWARD   And we need you. We're working together,
aren't we? As a team. We all need you.

FRANKIE?   Yea? Well why were you all laughing at me,
then?

HOWARD   Who? Who's laughing at you, Frankie?

*The others have long since stopped laughing in the presence of **Frankie**'s rage.*

FRANKIE   Them lot! You! You were showing me up in front of them lot and they were all laughing. Well I don't need you. I don't need any of you! And you don't need me – or this. YOU CAN STUFF YOUR PLAY!

*He makes to smash the lamp post. **Howard** makes a grab for it. They begin a tug of war. Howard manages to pull away the lamp post. **Frankie** makes a lunge but **Jay** steps in his way.*

JAY   Leave it, Frankie, it's not worth it.

Howard *stands the lamp post to one side.*

FRANKIE   *to **Jay***   Get away from me! Just leave me alone! Get away from me!

Jay *steps aside.*

Frankie *tries to get to his lamp post. **Howard** grabs him, pins him in a bear hug.*

HOWARD   Calm down. Please, Frankie, just steady on.

FRANKIE   *writhing, kicking*   Get off me! Get off! I mean it, I'll kill you. Get off! Give me it! I'LL KILL YOU!

*Finally, he lets out one long scream of frustrated anger and then hangs limp in **Howard**'s arms. **Howard** lets him go and he slides to the floor in a heap, sobbing. Pause.*

HOWARD   Carol, would you ask Elizabeth to come through? She's in the office, I think.

Carol *goes.*

TERRY   Is he crying?

HOWARD   Leave him, Terry, he'll be alright.

TERRY   He's crying, isn't he?

HOWARD   Come on now, Frankie, come on.

*Suddenly, with a yell, **Jay** runs at the lamp post, grabs it, lifts it high above his head and brings it down with a smash to the floor.*

HOWARD   Jay!

32

Jay picks it up and smashes it down repeatedly. It is breaking up, with pieces flying everywhere.

HOWARD   Jay! Get away!

Howard rushes at him but stops suddenly as Jay turns towards him, almost in tears of rage and hate.

JAY   SOD YOUR LAMP POST! Eh, Frankie? SOD HIM AND HIS LAMP POST!

Liz and Carol run in.

LIZ   What's happened? Frankie?   *she goes to him*

HOWARD   It's alright, Liz, it's—

LIZ   What's happened to him?

HOWARD   You lot, let's have you back next door. Come on, back next door and start putting everything away.   *to Jay*   And you . . . you will pick every scrap of this up, take it through next door and begin repairing it.

JAY   Oh will I?

HOWARD   Yes, you will!

LIZ   Howard. For goodness sake. Now look, Jay, if you've had an argument with Frankie and done this — *to the others*   Out! All of you!

HOWARD   Elizabeth, you've not got it quite right.

LIZ   Then you can explain it to me, then, can't you? Take this lot out first and then we'll talk about it.

Howard ushers out the group.

LIZ   *to Jay*   You know he just about worships you, don't you? Get this mess cleaned up and then you apologise.

Liz goes out. Pause.

JAY   You OK?

FRANKIE   Yes. Thanks, Jay.

JAY   Forget it.

Frankie begins to come round.

JAY   What a place, eh? What a place.

FRANKIE   Yes. What do they know, eh?

33

JAY   They really screw you up. Everywhere you go, people just . . . oh, I don't know.

FRANKIE   I know what you mean.

JAY   Don't they, though? When the day comes that I don't have to stay in a place like this – when that day finally comes I'll just. . . .

FRANKIE   It's not too far away.

JAY   Next summer. Next summer.

FRANKIE   Not long.

JAY   I'm just gonna go. Hitch hike. Europe. Wherever the road takes me. Just take a sleeping bag and a tent and go.

FRANKIE   Sounds good.

JAY   You bet. I'll get a labouring job first, get some cash and then I'm away, leave all this behind me.

FRANKIE   I wish I could go.

JAY   Come with me.

FRANKIE   I can't, can I? I've got to stay in care for years yet.

JAY   Just come with me. I'll get the money together, let you know when I've set it all up and we'll be away before they know what's hit 'em.

FRANKIE   You can't do that, though. There's papers to sign, passports.

JAY   Oh, I'll get it all sorted out.

FRANKIE   I wish we could go away.

JAY   We will.

FRANKIE   Promise.

JAY   What? Yes.

FRANKIE   Say it, say you promise.

JAY   Don't be daft.

Howard enters.

HOWARD   You. Out.

34

*Jay goes out. **Howard** walks over to **Frankie** but he turns away. **Howard** picks up the lamp post and goes out. In a while, **Terry**, **Carol**, **Margery** and **Barry** enter, without 'costumes'. **Margery** has the old doll.*

TERRY Aren't we doing the seance now?

MARGERY Yes, we're still doing it, aren't we? Tonight?

CAROL I'm not.

TERRY Don't come, then.

CAROL Anything could happen.

MARGERY Do you believe in it, then?

CAROL I don't know.

TERRY Oooooooh.

CAROL Gerroff.

TERRY She's scared.

CAROL I'm not.

MARGERY It most likely won't work. Brenda might have made it all up.

CAROL And if it does work?

TERRY Aahh, she's scared.

CAROL Am I?

TERRY They're good, ghosts. They can walk through walls and things.

He demonstrates, cracking his head on the wall. They laugh. He laughs and does it again.

MARGERY *to **Carol*** Don't you want to know if there is anything? If there is anything else?

CAROL Not really.

MARGERY There must be. There's got to be something other than this.

CAROL Why?

MARGERY Because if this is all there is I might as well be dead.

Pause.

35

TERRY   What do you want to be dead for?

Howard enters

TERRY   Howard, why does that Jacob Marley have to walk around for ever in those chains?

HOWARD   That was his punishment for being like he was when he was alive.

TERRY   Nasty and selfish, you mean?

HOWARD   That's right.

TERRY   He wasn't allowed to go to heaven?

HOWARD   Oh no.

TERRY   Why didn't he go to hell then?

HOWARD   Because he had to stay here to warn others about what would happen to them if they were selfish.

TERRY   Did Scrooge go to heaven in the end?

HOWARD   I suppose so.

TERRY   And Tiny Tim?

HOWARD   Yes.

MARGERY   So ghosts are dead people who aren't allowed to go to heaven or hell because they've done something wrong?

HOWARD   It's just a story, Margery.

TERRY   We're not allowed to talk about real ghosts, are we, because of Brenda?

HOWARD   I don't think there's any need for people to frighten themselves over something that doesn't exist.

MARGERY   You don't believe in them?

HOWARD   No I don't, and that's enough on that subject, thank you.

Jay appears in the doorway.

JAY   *in a loud whisper*   Hey, Liz's boyfriend is here.

HOWARD   Did you say something?

JAY   Who, me?   *looks at* **Terry**   No, it's him, he's a ventriloquist.

TERRY   A what?

JAY   Nothing.

36

TERRY   What's one of them? Is it rude?

JAY   It's someone who can talk without moving their lips.

TERRY   Can I do that?   *through clenched teeth*   Can I do that? Yes you can. Can I? Yes. Oh, good.

HOWARD   Alright, Terry.

TERRY   *through clenched teeth*   Don't talk to me like that, young man.

HOWARD   Stop it.

TERRY   *pointing at* **Barry**   That weren't me, it were him.

Liz enters.

TERRY   *through clenched teeth*   Hello, gorgeous, how's about a date?

They laugh.

HOWARD   Terry.

LIZ   *to* **Howard**   Can I have a word?

HOWARD   Sure.   *he follows* **Liz** *out*

JAY   Everybody in our room as soon as he's been round and we hear him go back downstairs.

CAROL   It's alright for you. If we get caught out of our room —

JAY   It's safe.

CAROL   It's easy for you to say.

JAY   Look, where else can we do it?

CAROL   I don't know that we should.

TERRY   Don't start all that again.

Howard enters.

HOWARD   Start what?

JAY   Is Lizzy a bit busy, then?

HOWARD   That'll do. Right, we'll call it a day.

They begin to move out.

HOWARD   Where are you going?

JAY Bed.

HOWARD Just a minute. What are you up to?

JAY Nothing. *pretends to yawn* See?

HOWARD Well I'm warning you.

TERRY *through clenched teeth* I am the ghost of Jacob Marley.

The group glare at him.

TERRY Who said that? Where did that come from? What are you all looking at me for? It weren't me. *laughs* It was really.

HOWARD Come on.

*They leave, **Frankie** last. **Howard** checks around the room, bolts the French window. **Liz** enters with her coat.*

LIZ You don't mind? I won't be long.

HOWARD I don't mind.

LIZ Only a few minutes. We'll be sat in the car. Only, we have to get this sorted out, we have to talk it out.

HOWARD Seeing too much of this place and not enough of him?

LIZ Something like that.

HOWARD Go on, off you go.

LIZ Thanks. I've just had a quick look in at Brenda. She's fine.

*Liz goes out. **Howard** shakes a couple of cushions, looks around again, goes out, putting out the light.*

SCENE 4

The boys' bedroom, late that night. **Jay** *and* **Terry** *are making space for the seance.* **Barry** *is sat on the floor,* **Frankie** *is stood some way from them.*

JAY   *producing a candle from his pocket*   Da da!

TERRY   Hey, where'd you get the candle?

JAY   Pinched it from the store cupboard.

TERRY   That's great, just what we need.

JAY   Come on, we've got to get the spirits moving. Sit down. Come on, Frankie, it's just a game.   *they sit in a circle*   Is there anybody there?   *tries another voice, very theatrical*   Is there anybody there?   *they laugh*   No, come on, do it properly. Is there anybody there?

A knock knock.

JAY   That was quick.

The door opens. **Carol** *and* **Margery** *enter.*

JAY   Come on, girls.

They join the ring. **Jay** *lights the candle.*

JAY   If there is anybody there, please give us a sign. Three knocks for yes, two for no.

Frankie *laughs,* **Terry** *joins in.*

JAY   *to* **Terry**   What are you laughing at?

TERRY I dunno.

FRANKIE How can the ghost knock twice to tell you it's not there, if it's not there?

JAY Eh? Oh yes, slight problem. Right, everybody concentrate. Try really hard to concentrate. *very theatrically* If there is anybody there, please give us a sign. We are ready to communicate. You will come to us. You WILL come to us. We are waiting for you. We are ready. You cannot refuse, we will not be refused. We are waiting, our patience will not last. Show yourself now!

He pretends to be suddenly possessed.

JAY Ooooooooaaaaaaahhhhhhh!

ALL Oh, Jay! etc.

JAY No, sorry, serious now. I won't do it again, honest. Come on, do it properly this time. Get concentrating, close your eyes to get the vibes.

*They do so. **Jay** coughs over the candle and blows it out.*

JAY Hey!

They open their eyes.

JAY Who did that, eh?

He looks upwards, they follow.

JAY Who's blown the candle out? Something's in the air. Matches, come on. *pause* Terry?

TERRY What?

JAY Didn't you want to go to the toilet?

TERRY No.

Jay glares at him.

TERRY Oh yes.

He gets up and goes out. The candle is lit again.

JAY I'm going to ask you, spirit, to show yourself for the last time.

*Suddenly **Brenda** bursts in. The girls scream.*

FRANKIE It's alright, it's only Brenda.

40

JAY *to* **Carol**, *who has screamed in his ear*   Don't do that!

CAROL   Come on, Brenda, join in.

BRENDA   You're calling her, aren't you?

JAY   Yes.

BRENDA   She will come.

JAY   Yes, we're getting the vibes. Join in.

BRENDA   You mustn't.

JAY   You want us to believe you, don't you?

BRENDA   You don't know what you're doing.

JAY   We do.

BRENDA   You'll see.

JAY   That's the idea.

MARGERY   Yes, we want to see, we want to.

JAY   Look, if you're stopping, join in. If not, get back to bed.

BRENDA   I'm telling.

JAY   *springing up*   Oh yea?

Brenda turns to face him.

JAY   Go on, then, go and tell.

They are face to face. Jay is daring her. She turns to go but he grabs her arm. She cannot break free from his grip.

BRENDA   Let go of me!

JAY   You started all this.

BRENDA   Let go of me or I'll scream.

JAY   You do and I'll say this was all your idea. I'll say you screamed because you pretended to see the ghost again to frighten us.

BRENDA   I didn't pretend before. I did see her. You wouldn't say that.

JAY   Try me.

Jay lets go of her. Still face to face.

JAY   Go on, then, go and tell.

41

Brenda dare not move now. The atmosphere has changed. The mood is serious. Jay rejoins the ring.

JAY   Right. Concentrate. Spirit you will show yourself.

There is a tension in the air now, all feel as if they know something is about to happen.

·JAY   I am now going to count down from ten to zero and when I reach zero you will show yourself. Can we all join hands, please? Let us combine our power.

They all join hands. The ring is complete but for Jay and Frankie. Slowly Jay begins the countdown. His voice is full of confident power. He is no longer joking but willing something to happen, commanding it.

JAY   Ten . . . Nine . . . Eight . . . Seven . . . Six . . . you are nearer to us, I feel your presence . . . Five . . . Four . . . Three . . . you are close, you are about to give us a sign . . . Two . . . you are almost with us . . . One. Come to us, it is time, the spirit is here . . . ZERO!

Jay grabs Frankie's hand. Contact. The shock hits them all. The effect is overwhelming. The joke has gone badly wrong. The girls are hysterical, screaming, almost sick with fear. The boys too are caught up in it. Barry is shaking uncontrollably. Even Jay, who for a split second after contact was laughing, is now scared. Brenda, outside the ring, is in some kind of trance, rigid, staring into the centre of the ring, as if she really can see someone there. Gradually the screaming subsides, but this only serves to make them aware of Brenda as she slowly, reluctantly moves forward, into the ring.

BRENDA   Mummy, I love you. Please, Mummy, I can't come with you. Let me stay here. Mummy, please, no!

Watching this, the others begin to cry out again, screaming for her to stop whatever it is she is doing. Jay grabs her, shaking her violently, shouting at her to stop it. Finally, he manages to pull her away, and together they fall outside the ring. As they hit the floor the candle goes out and the screaming stops suddenly. Darkness. Silence. A whimper and a sob and then silence.

42

SCENE 5

The main room, the next afternoon. **Howard** *is sitting on the sofa.* **Liz** *is at the table. A* **social worker** *is seated opposite her. There is a long pause before anyone speaks.*

SOCIAL WORKER   I don't know how you managed to get them all off to school.

HOWARD   All but three.

SOCIAL WORKER   And they all say they saw something last night?

HOWARD   Not all of them, no.

SOCIAL WORKER   Oh?   *she looks at* **Liz**

LIZ   Terry. He wasn't there.

SOCIAL WORKER   Where was he?

HOWARD   We found him unconscious on the bathroom floor with a sheet over his head.

Liz glares at him, but he doesn't notice.

SOCIAL WORKER   What?

HOWARD   He walked into the wall and knocked himself out.

Pause. This time **Howard** *catches* **Liz's** *look. The 'phone is heard ringing somewhere in the house.* **Howard** *and* **Liz** *jump up to answer it, but* **Howard** *wins. He is glad to get out.*

HOWARD   Excuse me.

He is gone.

SOCIAL WORKER   I think you've got to try not to be automatically on the defensive, Liz, and be realistic about what we have to do. I know some strong words have been said to you this morning but you must have known it was coming, and nobody is thinking of anything else but what is best for the children. You're tired. I don't just mean from last night, either. There's nothing sinister in suggesting you take a holiday.

Howard returns.

HOWARD   *to the social worker*   It's for you.

*She goes out. Pause. **Howard** watches **Liz**. She is sealing some envelopes.*

HOWARD   Look, you're good at your job and this is a good home. We've made it a happy home for some of them. Well, not happy, maybe. Safe. You've made it a safe place. They've felt secure. Haven't they?

LIZ   What are you telling me for? If that's what you think, tell her.

HOWARD   You're giving in, aren't you?

LIZ   You know social services are going to do exactly what they want.

HOWARD   You can't let them take apart what you have built.

LIZ   It's a pity you didn't open your mouth and say this this morning when we had wall to wall social workers, given me some support then. I don't need it now, Howard, it's too late.

She moves to the French windows.

HOWARD   Where are you going?

LIZ   Post some letters.

HOWARD   What about her?

LIZ   You save us. You talk to her. See if you can put a few words together without you putting your other foot in your mouth.

HOWARD   Oh, thanks.

44

LIZ I've said all I want to say. I've tried. Anyway, she's right, I am tired. I do need to get away.

HOWARD Yea, and when you get back they'll have fixed you up a nice office job somewhere and this place will be turned into a nursing home.

*Liz goes out into the garden. **Howard** picks up a comic, tries to read, throws it away, bored. The **social worker** returns.*

SOCIAL WORKER Where's Liz?

HOWARD She's just taking a bit of a walk, down to the post box.

SOCIAL WORKER Oh.

Pause.

HOWARD She won't be long. *pause* Was that, er, the office?

SOCIAL WORKER Yes.

*Pause. **Terry** enters from the hall with a jug of water. He is in his pyjamas and dressing gown and has a plaster on his forehead. He stops as they look at him.*

TERRY I'm allowed to.

HOWARD Allowed to what, Terry?

TERRY Water the flower. It's my turn today.

HOWARD Not now.

SOCIAL WORKER It's alright. I wanted to have a quiet word with Liz. I'll catch her up.

*She goes into the garden. **Howard** clears away some coffee cups. **Terry** waters the flower. **Howard** takes out the cups. **Terry** moves to the centre of the room, kneels, puts down the jug, crosses himself and begins to pray.*

TERRY Our Father, who art in heaven, hallowed be thy name, for thine is the kingdom, the power and the glory, for ever and ever, amen.

*He crosses himself again, picks up the jug, stands, and begins to assume a priest-like walk about, sprinkling water onto the walls, floor, ceiling, table . . . The **social worker** steps in through the French windows.*

SOCIAL WORKER   I'll take my coat, its a bit – What
are you doing?

TERRY   Sprinkling holy water.

SOCIAL WORKER   Should you be doing that?

TERRY   Yes, I've got to.

SOCIAL WORKER   I think you'd better give me that
jug.

TERRY   I haven't finished yet.

SOCIAL WORKER   Come on.

TERRY   I've seen it on films, this.

SOCIAL WORKER   You're wetting everything.

TERRY   It makes everything pure and clean.

He sprinkles some on her.

SOCIAL WORKER   Stop it! Get away!

Terry *laughs and does it again.*

SOCIAL WORKER   Right.

She makes to go through into the hall.

TERRY   *Blocking her way*   Don't tell.

SOCIAL WORKER   Get out of my way.   *calls*
Howard!

TERRY   Don't tell, please.

SOCIAL WORKER   Give me the jug.

TERRY   Let me finish.

SOCIAL WORKER   Give it to me! Get out of the way,
you fool.

She has made a mistake, but it is too late to apologise.
Terry *tips all the remaining water over her. She screams.*

TERRY   I'm sorry, I'm sorry.

She is gasping. ***Terry*** *puts the jug down and grabs a
cushion. He begins to dab her chest with it.*

SOCIAL WORKER   Ah! Get away from me!

TERRY   I'm sorry.

Howard *enters, wiping his hands on a tea towel.*

46

HOWARD   Terry! What are you doing?

SOCIAL WORKER   He threw a jug of water at me.

HOWARD   What the hell did you do that for? Terry, stop doing that, now!

Terry stops dabbing her with the cushion and clutches it to him, biting it hard, his face shaking with the effort.

SOCIAL WORKER   Look at me!

HOWARD   Terry.

SOCIAL WORKER   What am I going to do? It's gone right through.

TERRY   Have you wet your knickers?

SOCIAL WORKER   Ooh!

She storms out.

HOWARD   I'm sorry. Look, can I –?

SOCIAL WORKER   *off stage*   Tell Liz I'll ring.

HOWARD   *off*   Yes. Sure. 'Bye, then.   *to **Terry*** What's the matter with you? What the hell did you throw that at her for? *pause* Terry? *pause* Are you going to tell me or am I going to make you stay in your room? Well? Put that cushion down!

***Howard** pulls the cushion from **Terry**'s mouth and flings it across the room.*

TERRY   I want to go to my room.

HOWARD   Now look, Terry, what you've done is wrong. You know that, don't you?

Terry nods.

HOWARD   Why?

TERRY   Because it's naughty and you shouldn't throw water at people.

HOWARD   Why did you do it?   *pause*   Are you going to tell me? You want to stay in your room?

TERRY   Yes.

HOWARD   Right. You'll do that. You'll stay up there until I say you can come down. In fact, no, you can mop all this up first. Why should we do it? You clean it up and then get to your room.

TERRY   No.

HOWARD   What?

TERRY   It's not supposed to be mopped up. You're supposed to leave it.

HOWARD   You are mopping it up.

TERRY   I can't!

HOWARD   Can't?

TERRY   I won't! It won't work if you clean it up!

HOWARD   What won't work?

TERRY   You shouldn't ask me that. You're not allowed to ask me that!

HOWARD   What are you talking about?   *drops tea towel*   Get mopping.

TERRY   I'm not doing it! I'm not!

HOWARD   Right, get to your room now! Go on! We'll see how long you stay there until you start being sensible!

Howard begins to push Terry out of the room.

TERRY   *resisting*   Don't wipe it up! You've got to leave it!   *struggling as he is being pushed out*   YOU'RE A BLOODY BUGGER YOU! Jay told me them words. You BLOODY BUGGER.

HOWARD   Get upstairs!

TERRY   *off*   I HATE YOU! You bloody blooder!

He continues to curse and protest his way upstairs. Howard mops up the water. Frankie enters from the garden.

FRANKIE   What was all that about?

HOWARD   Oh, hi, Frankie. You're home early.

FRANKIE   They let me come home. I didn't feel very well.

HOWARD   What's wrong?

48

FRANKIE   Migraine.

HOWARD   They let you home?

FRANKIE   Did Terry do all this?

HOWARD   Yes. Got himself worked up again.

FRANKIE   What's going to happen, about last night?

HOWARD   I don't know, Frankie. We'll just have to wait and see.

FRANKIE   You won't get into trouble, will you? You and Liz? I mean from the council. It wasn't your fault.

HOWARD   I don't know.

Liz enters. The walk hasn't improved her mood.

LIZ   I had an escort home. Didn't I Frankie?

She sees the water.

HOWARD   It's only water. Terry.

LIZ   Where is she?

HOWARD   She went. Said she'd ring.

FRANKIE   Who? Who's been?

LIZ   Did you manage to say anything?

HOWARD   A bit.   *makes to take out the cloth*   I just said what I thought.

He goes out.

FRANKIE   Was that letter about another job?

LIZ   No. Please, Frankie.

She sits. Miserable and worried.

FRANKIE   Don't leave us, Liz. You can't leave.

A thumping and crashing comes from upstairs.

LIZ   No, I won't leave you.   *pause*   What are we going to do, eh Frankie?

FRANKIE   Just don't leave.

HOWARD   *off stage*   Shut up, Terry!

The noise subsides a little.

FRANKIE   We think a lot about you. You should know that. You mean a lot to us. You mean a lot to me.

49

*An agonizing pause. **Frankie** is close to her. He wants to offer some comfort but doesn't know how. **Liz** is deep in her own thoughts. He tentatively puts his hand on her shoulder.*

FRANKIE Don't worry, Liz. We'll think of something. We can take care of things. We think a lot about you. More than you know. I do. I think about you a lot.

***Frankie** is confused. It is part wanting to comfort her and part something else. He slips his arm round her.*

LIZ *suddenly startled* Frankie! *pulling away* What are you doing! What are you doing, Frankie?

FRANKIE I'm only –

LIZ What do you – Oh damn! What's happening in this place?

FRANKIE Don't you like me?

LIZ What?

FRANKIE Don't you like me?

LIZ Of course I do, but –

FRANKIE Aren't I special?

LIZ No more than any of the others.

FRANKIE I thought I might be special to you. I thought we were more than just friends. I love you!

***Terry** starts crashing about upstairs again.*

LIZ Oh no.

FRANKIE *almost angry* I can't help it!

LIZ Oh, Frankie, no.

FRANKIE Don't say that. *he moves towards her* Please, Liz, I –

LIZ Don't, Frankie. Get away. Go away! Get out!

FRANKIE You want me to go?

LIZ Yes!

***Frankie** looks at her. His love turns to hate. He turns and runs out into the garden.*

LIZ Frankie! Oh damn!

HOWARD *off* Terry, will you stop that banging, now!

TERRY *off* No!

HOWARD *off* Do you want me to come up there and sort you out?

TERRY *off* You can't. I've made it so you can't get in.

HOWARD *off* What are you doing?

TERRY *off* I'm building a rocket!

HOWARD *off* What?

TERRY *off* I'm building a rocket and I'm going to get in it and I'm going to be a spaceman and go to Pluto 'cause I don't like it here any more!

HOWARD *off* Terry!

Howard appears at the door.

HOWARD Frankie's school's just been on the 'phone. He didn't turn up for lessons this afternoon.

LIZ No headache?

HOWARD No.

LIZ Great. Get him for me, will you, Howard? He's just gone out. Did you tell them he'd turned up here?

HOWARD Yes.

LIZ OK. I'll deal with it. Thanks.

Brenda and Margery appear at the door, in nightdresses and dressing gowns.

HOWARD What are you doing up?

BRENDA We can't rest, can we? Not with that noise. Can we sit in here?

HOWARD No.

LIZ It's OK, Howard. They'll be alright. Will you ask Frankie to wait in the office?

HOWARD Yes.

He goes into the garden.

LIZ Come in, girls.

BRENDA Thanks, Liz.

LIZ How are you?

BRENDA   Not very well.

LIZ   Margery?

BRENDA   She's a bit better.

LIZ   Both well enough to come downstairs.

Terry is crashing about again.

LIZ   Oh, for God's sake!

She goes out. Brenda begins to look about the room. The noise from upstairs stops.

MARGERY   What are you doing?

BRENDA   Seeing where we can hide the box.

MARGERY   I hope it works.

BRENDA   I hope so.

MARGERY   Do you think we'll get everyone to put something in it?

BRENDA   We all have to. Everybody has to put something precious in it, something they treasure, something they care for lots. Jewels, trinkets, money, anything. And we'll put the doll in it.

MARGERY   Must we put the doll in?

BRENDA   It's an offering, isn't it? You see, if we give the ghost the box with all the things we value most, then it's an offering. It'll please her and then maybe she'll be happy and won't come back again.

MARGERY   She'll know we're trying to help her.

BRENDA   Like in olden times they used to bring things to the altar for the gods, to please them. It's the same thing.

MARGERY   What are you putting in?

BRENDA   I can't tell you that. It's private. It's secret. We mustn't know what each of us puts in. Nobody must look at what the others are putting in. Then we'll seal it up and hide it somewhere. Tonight. It has to be done for tonight.

MARGERY   Brenda, I'm frightened.

BRENDA   Why?

52

MARGERY I just am.

BRENDA They don't believe us, you know.

MARGERY I know.

BRENDA We've got to do it.

MARGERY I don't want to stay here any more. I don't like it here any more.

BRENDA We don't have any choice about where we stay. We never have had. They put us in whatever home they want.

MARGERY I want to be in my home! *pause* I wish . . . I wish my Mum loved me, like she did once, like it used to be.

BRENDA Who needs other people? Who needs them? We can sort this out ourselves. We can get by without them. Older people are never what you think they are. You can't trust them, any of them. You can't rely on them, even parents. You spend years respecting them, admiring them. *pause* I used to think my Dad was perfect. One day you find out. They're not what you thought they were at all. How could somebody pretend to love us and then leave and make my Mum not want to live any more? I hate all their lies. Pretending to be something they're not. It's all a show.

MARGERY When you're little you pretend to yourself. When you're grown up you pretend to everyone else.

BRENDA Yes.

MARGERY I still love her.

BRENDA You only love what she was.

MARGERY No. She thinks I only love her for the way it used to be, but I do, I do love her. It doesn't matter what she is, what she pretends.

BRENDA She doesn't want you. How can you love someone that's kicked you out and put you in here?

MARGERY She couldn't help it, she had, to, we –

BRENDA Now who's pretending? Who's pretending now? She's kicked you out. She doesn't want you.

MARGERY She does!

53

BRENDA You're an embarrassment to her. She doesn't want you around when she's entertaining.

Margery flies at Brenda, lashing out. They fight ferociously.

MARGERY Don't say that! You're a liar, you're a liar!

BRENDA Am I? Your mother's a tramp!

MARGERY You filthy liar!

BRENDA Oh no I'm not, it's the truth!

Liz rushes in and tries to stop them.

LIZ Hey! Stop it! Come on, that'll do now! Stop it!

She manages to pull them apart.

The fury of the fight has left the two girls tense and shocked. Margery is trying hard but failing to keep back sobs. Brenda is holding on better, trying to act the winner.

BRENDA You just can't accept it, can you? It's time you grew up!

LIZ *to Brenda* Get upstairs, now!

Brenda turns to go, but stops on hearing Howard run in from the garden.

HOWARD Just a minute. *to Liz* Nowhere.

LIZ You sure?

HOWARD Have either of you two seen Frankie? *pause* Well?

BRENDA Has he run away?

HOWARD Have you seen him?

BRENDA No.

HOWARD Margery?

MARGERY No.

HOWARD Oh no.

He runs through and into the hall.

BRENDA Has he run away?

LIZ Get upstairs!

54

*Brenda goes out. Liz comforts Margery who is still
sobbing.*

LIZ What happened?

MARGERY She was telling lies.

LIZ Do you want to tell me about it?

MARGERY Why do you pretend to be nice to me?

LIZ Do I?

MARGERY You all do.

LIZ No we don't.

MARGERY Everybody lies to me.

LIZ Margery.

Howard comes back in, with his jacket.

HOWARD I'll take the car and have a look round the
estate.

He goes out again.

MARGERY I'm going to run away.

LIZ Margery.

Margery I am.

LIZ Come on, let's go and find you something.

MARGERY Something to play with? You want me to
play? You think it makes things easy for me, don't you?
You think it helps push everything else out of
here. *holds her head* None of you know what's going
on in here. My thoughts are my own and no one can take
them away! I hate you and I hate this ghost house!

Pause.

LIZ And you think running away will solve anything?

Pause.

MARGERY *quietly* Yes.

LIZ *softly* Really? Do you?

MARGERY Why did Brenda say those things? About
my Mum? She shouldn't say things like that, they're not
true.

*Pause.   **Margery** looks at **Liz**. She is lost and lonely. **Liz** draws her to her and she cries freely on her shoulder.   Pause.*

LIZ   Come on.

Liz takes her gently out of the room.

SCENE 6

A few hours later, the main room. **Barry** *is sat in his chair with his radio.* **Jay** *is stood by the window.* **Terry** *enters from the hall.*

TERRY   What's up, Jay?   *pause*   Were you scared last night?   *pause*   I wasn't.   *pause*   I was just pretending to be scared so the girls would be more frightened.   *pause*   Me and my Dad saw a ghost once when we were on holiday in Wales. In a monastery. It was a monk all dressed in –

JAY   Shut up!

Pause. **Barry** *twiddles with his radio, puts it back to his ear.*

TERRY   Were you scared, Jay?

JAY   If you've opened your mouth about what happened I'll –

TERRY   No! No! I haven't, honest.

JAY   You'd better not have.

TERRY   Is it to be a secret?

JAY   You heard what I said.

Carol and **Brenda** *enter.* **Brenda** *has the box.*

JAY   Don't ask me to put anything in there.

BRENDA   Who's asking you?

JAY   Daft idea.

CAROL   What else can we do?

TERRY   What's in it now?

57

BRENDA   You can't look. Everyone's put something special in.

TERRY   *trying to look in*   What's that?

BRENDA   Nothing.

TERRY   That's Margery's crummy tea pot holder.

BRENDA   No it's not.

TERRY   Yes it is, I saw it. If she's only putting that in then I'm taking out my aeroplane and my ten pence.

BRENDA   No.

TERRY   She's only put that in and that's my favourite bomber.

CAROL   You can't change it.

TERRY   It's not fair. What's a ghost going to do with a tea pot holder?

CAROL   It's not going to do anything with it. It's an offering, isn't it? Something she treasures.

JAY   *to Terry*   What's a ghost going to do with an Airfix bomber?

BRENDA   You know what we're trying to do. Don't spoil it.

TERRY   I bet no one else has put money in, only me.

BRENDA   They have.

JAY   I thought you weren't supposed to know what each person puts in?

BRENDA   Money's different.

JAY   Ha!

Barry gets out of his chair, walks over to the girls and holds out his radio for them.

BRENDA   I think he wants to give us his radio.

CAROL   Do you think we should?

BRENDA   I don't know.

CAROL   It's all you've got, Barry.

He gives it to Carol.

CAROL   Thanks, Barry.

58

BRENDA Thanks, Barry.

The radio goes in the box. **Barry** *returns to his chair.*

JAY What are you going to do with it all? Just hide it and hope the ghost's going to find it and say 'thank you very much' and leave with it?

BRENDA We're not asking you to have anything to do with it, are we? You think you're great, don't you? Well I've got news for you, nobody else does. Not now Frankie's gone. *to* **Carol** Come on, I know where we can hide it.

BRENDA *to Jay* And don't you look.

JAY Oh, go dig a hole and bury yourself.

The girls go through into the hall.

TERRY Jay? You know Frankie? If he wasn't scared, why did he run away?

JAY I don't know. Girl trouble, maybe.

TERRY What's that? Oh, you mean 'doing them things'? Which girl?

JAY I never found out.

TERRY A bit funny, Frankie, wasn't he?

JAY Leave it, will you?

TERRY I mean, I don't know him really, only just –

JAY No! You don't know him!

Pause.

TERRY Will they have tracker dogs out looking for him?

JAY Yea. They've got these hounds, like fox hounds, and when they catch him they'll tear him to pieces.

BARRY *singing softly to himself*
Brown girl in the ring, tra la la la la
Brown girl in the ring, tra la la la la la la.

JAY And then they hang his head on a fence.

TERRY I'm not going to run away. I'm not scared.

JAY Frankie wasn't scared!

Howard*, ***Liz** *and* **Margery** *enter.* **Liz** *has a sheet of paper.*

59

LIZ   Where are the girls?

JAY   Don't know.

TERRY   They went down the hall, that way.

JAY   I'll fetch them.

HOWARD   Stay where you are.

TERRY   *jumping up*   I'll go.

He runs out into the hall.

JAY   *seeing the paper*   What's this, then?

LIZ   It's a list of points regarding general conduct.

JAY   Rules.

LIZ   If you like.

JAY   We've got enough already.

LIZ   These are amendments to present rules.

JAY   I can't read.

LIZ   I'm going to read them out to everyone.

Jay makes for the door.

LIZ   Now where are you going?

Howard blocks his way.

JAY   Games room. If I can get past your securicor.

HOWARD   You'll stay right here.

JAY   I don't have to listen to you. I don't want your rules
and regulations. That's all I ever get. We're all supposed
to make up the rules together, aren't we? You're
supposed to –

LIZ   You can't keep to your own rules! We all set them up
together and you –

JAY   So now you're just making them up without asking
us?

Terry enters with the girls.

HOWARD   Listen, Jay, listen all of you. All we want to
do is make it so that everyone starts to think about each
other. We want you to consider yourselves and each
other.

JAY   Huh.

TERRY *singing* Consider yourself at home.

JAY *catching on, joining in* Consider yourself one of the family . . .

HOWARD Stop it.

Jay begins to do a little jig.

JAY We don't want to have no fuss . . . di da di da . . .

Howard runs at him. Jay stops suddenly, squaring up to him.

JAY Go on, then, go on! Hit me!

*Howard stops, furious. He turns, strides back to **Liz**, snatches the paper from her.*

HOWARD *reading* Number one!

Jay puts his fingers in his ears. Glares at the others.

JAY Do it!

One by one they follow suit, Terry last.

TERRY Are we having a fag?

HOWARD *shouting* Number one! Everyone must make sure –

TERRY What's he saying, Jay?

OTHERS What? What's he saying? etc.

HOWARD Everyone must make sure that the lights –

JAY Fights?

TERRY What?

JAY Fights!

TERRY Are we allowed to have fights?

JAY Yea.

*Howard charges at **Jay**, grabs him and marches him out.*

TERRY They're going to have a fight!

He runs out after them.

Others Fight! Fight!

*The chant begins. They try to follow **Terry** but **Liz** is at the door. She tries to shut them up, but it isn't working. They just come back into the room, dancing and chanting with a frantic rhythm. **Liz** gives in, sits shattered. Gradually they notice and the chant subsides to silence. They wait.*

LIZ   I've never known anything like it. All of you! It's just disgraceful. I'm surprised at you! Now if you want to lose all your privileges you just carry on like you are doing. I can soon make you realize how stupid you are being. Now you WILL read these rules and you WILL abide by them. There is no place here for those who cannot accept the simplest rules of common decency.

***Terry** runs in.*

TERRY   Hey, I've just learnt a new swear word off Howard! He was calling Jay a . . .   *he sees everyone subdued*

LIZ   I'm going to pin this up in the hall and from that moment these rules apply, so make sure you've read them. Then I want all of you washed and into bed with lights out.

TERRY   Oh, it's not time yet, is it?

LIZ   You go to bed when I say so!

TERRY   We might see the ghost.

LIZ   Don't you ever mention that word to me again!

TERRY   You shouldn't make people frightened.

LIZ   You'd better behave yourselves, then, hadn't you?

She goes out. They all follow in silence.

SCENE 7

*The boys' bedroom, later. **Jay** is stood alone. Terry enters with his towel and toothbrush. He stops and watches **Jay**.*

TERRY   What are you thinking about, Jay?

JAY   The box.

TERRY   I said a prayer for it to work. Ghosts don't feel prickles, do they?

JAY   What?

TERRY   Holly prickles. They could walk through a holly bush if they wanted to, couldn't they?

JAY   I don't know. Get to sleep, Terry.   *pause*   Holly? What are you on about?

TERRY   That's where they've hid the box. I was watching.

JAY   You saw where they hid the box?

TERRY   Yes.

JAY   You sure you know where it is?

TERRY   Yes. Why?

JAY   Where?

TERRY   What?

JAY   I want that box. Where is it?

TERRY   What do you want it for?

JAY   Never mind.

TERRY   But what about the ghost?   *pause*   You're not going to steal it, are you?

63

JAY It's not stealing. I've a better use for it. Look, Terry, come on. You're my friend, aren't you?

TERRY Yes.

JAY And what are friends for?

TERRY Being nice to each other.

JAY Right. I want you to be nice to me. I want you to tell me where the box is.

TERRY I can't do that.

JAY Alright, then, if you don't want to be my friend.

TERRY Don't say that, Jay, please. Look I –

JAY Listen. There's no ghost, right? And if there is, this box can't stop it.

TERRY It might.

JAY Are you scared? Do you want me to give you any more cigarettes?

TERRY Yes but –

JAY Well, then?

TERRY No, Jay, please. Please don't make me tell you.

Pause.

JAY OK, if I tell you why I want it, you promise you will never tell anyone. Ever?

TERRY Honest, I promise.

He slits his throat with his finger.

JAY I want to help Frankie.

TERRY Frankie?

JAY Yes. There's some money in that box and things he might be able to sell. I think I know where he's hiding. I want to take it to him tonight.

TERRY Are you coming back? *pause* You wouldn't come back. I haven't got any other friends, Jay, I don't want to be lonely again.

JAY Frankie's on his own out there in the night. Scared to hell I should think. It's my fault. I didn't realize what I was doing . . . putting ideas into his head. I didn't think he'd do it. I've got to help him. Please, Terry. *pause* Well?

TERRY I think you're a very nice person. You're my only real friend because you think about other people.

JAY Never mind that. Will you help me?

TERRY No.

JAY OK. Forget it.

TERRY Please, Jay.

JAY Leave it. Get to sleep.

Pause. **Terry** *begins to cry.*

TERRY Aren't you my friend any more?

JAY No.

Pause.

TERRY If I tell you where it is will you take me with you?

JAY No.

TERRY Let me come with you. Please. I won't be any trouble. *pause* Come back, then, say you'll come come back. You can't leave me!

JAY Hey, sshhh. You'll wake the others. Look, Terry, I'm no good for you. I use you. You need protecting from people like me.

TERRY I know you make fun of me. I don't mind. I know you don't mean to be nasty.

Pause.

JAY I can't take you, Terry.

TERRY Will you come back? Ever?

Pause. **Terry** *is devastated.*

JAY OK.

TERRY Oh, Jay.

JAY OK. Come on, get your gear on. Where is it?

TERRY I . . . I'm scared, Jay.

JAY Come on, you've got me.

TERRY You won't run off without me, will you? If I tell you?

JAY No. We'll get it together. What's the matter?

TERRY I've got to get it.

JAY What?

TERRY You wait here.

JAY What for? Don't you trust me?

TERRY No.

JAY Thanks.

TERRY I mean, no, it's not that.

JAY What, then?

TERRY I'm the one who's breaking the magic, aren't I? The ghost knows. If I tell you, if I show you, if I get it, the ghost knows it's me. I'm the one who's broken the magic. I'm the one who's done wrong. I'm the one who has to pay.

JAY Don't be daft.

TERRY No, Jay. Stay here. Please. Wait for me.

He starts to search around.

JAY What are you doing?

TERRY I need my torch. I can't go down without my torch, can I? Oh, here you are. You were hiding from me, weren't you, you naughty torch.

Jay stops him.

JAY Thanks, Terry.

They shake hands.

TERRY I'm going, then.

Terry goes.

SCENE 8

*The main room, moonlight. **Margery** comes in, carrying the box. She is in her nightdress. She takes it over to the French window, undoes it and takes out the doll.*

MARGERY   There you are. I couldn't leave you in there all night, could I? I know how lonely and frightened you would be on your own. Never mind, you're safe now. I didn't want you to go in the box. I told them not to but they wouldn't listen. You see, I didn't want them to know that you were my special friend. They think I'm silly talking to dolls, they think it's for babies. But they don't understand, do they? You just cuddle up to me and get warm. You've been crying, haven't you? All your little eyelashes are stuck together. I bet you thought we were never going to see each other again, didn't you?

***Terry** appears. He shines his torch in **Margery's** face.*

TERRY   What are you doing here?

MARGERY   Nothing. Nothing. Don't come near me.

TERRY   You've got the box.

MARGERY   Don't hurt me. Please. I was going to put it back. I was, I was.

TERRY   Shut up, will you? Ssshhh.

MARGERY   I only wanted to see the doll. I'll put the box back. Let me put it back.

TERRY   Give it to me.

MARGERY   No! Stay away from me.

TERRY Don't shout. You've got to give it to me. I need it.

MARGERY Please.

TERRY Don't make a noise. Look I want the box. It shouldn't be like this. This isn't supposed to happen. Give it me!

MARGERY You're not taking it. Don't touch me!

Terry snatches the box. They struggle. He pulls it away from her and starts to go.

MARGERY Don't tell! Don't tell Brenda. Please!

She starts to cry. Terry stops.

TERRY Shut up. Shut up, will you? You'll wake everybody up!

Margery tries to stop herself but cannot. Terry puts down the box and moves towards her. A look of horror comes into her eyes.

MARGERY No! No, please, don't hurt me. I don't want to. You –

TERRY It's alright. Don't make a noise. Keep quiet and you won't get hurt! *he tries to put his hand over her mouth to shut her up*

Margery is petrified. Terry is panicking. She lets out a stifled scream. Terry smashes the torch down onto her head.

TERRY Shut up!

They tumble together into the hall and we hear him hit her again. Pause. Silence. In a while he comes into the room, picks up the box, stands shaking.

TERRY You shouldn't have screamed. You shouldn't have made me do that. You should have given me the box. You shouldn't have made me do that.

Jay runs in.

JAY Where were you? *he sees the box* Good lad, Terry, good lad. *he takes it* Let's have a look, then, see what we can use.

Quickly he begins to search through, throwing unwanted items out.

JAY   Rubbish.   *throws out the doll*   Money. Money . . . yes, here. Great. All this lot is rubbish. This is no good.

*Out go **Terry's** aeroplane, **Margery's** tea pot holder.*

JAY   Ah! *he takes out **Barry's** radio*   Might be able to sell this.   *he tries it, shakes it*   It doesn't work .   *opens back*   There's no batteries. It never even had any batteries. All this time he's been sat listening to this and it's got no bloody batteries!

Terry collapses and begins to sob uncontrollably.

JAY   Shut up! What's the matter? You got it, didn't you? You seen the ghost?

TERRY   She wouldn't keep quiet.

JAY   What?

TERRY   I asked her to keep quiet but she wouldn't. I didn't mean it, Jay, honest, I didn't mean to do it.

JAY   Do what? What are you talking about?

TERRY   It was supposed to be in the store cupboard. That's where they hid it. Under the plastic holly for the ghost of Christmas Present's costume. But she had it. Margery. She had the box and she wouldn't give it to me. She wouldn't keep quiet so I hit her.

JAY   Oh God! What have you done?

TERRY   I've put her in the store cupboard.

Jay runs out to see, comes back in again.

TERRY   What have I done?

JAY   Get upstairs, Terry. Get in bed. Say nothing. Let me run, let them think it's me. Go on, go!

Terry is rooted to the spot.

JAY   Do you want to go in hospital again for Christ's sake!

Slaps him to bring him round.

JAY   Move!

TERRY   I can't.

JAY   Come on, Terry, lean on me. Come on, you can do it. I'll help you.

TERRY   I'm sorry, Jay, I'm sorry.

JAY   It'll be alright.

There is noise from elsewhere in the house. Voices, running on the landing.

TERRY   They're coming, Jay, they're coming. I can't. Go on, you go.

JAY   No. Come on!

TERRY   Please Jay, go!

JAY   Keep quiet, OK? Say nothing, Terry. You hear me? Tell them nothing. Thanks, Terry.

Carol runs in.

CAROL   What's going on?

Jay runs to the French window, struggles to open it.

CAROL   You've been in the box! You've robbed the box! He's getting away! He stole the box, he's getting away!

Jay gives up on the window, runs back to the door, pushing Carol and sending her sprawling. He dashes out.

HOWARD   *off stage*   What the hell's going on? Hey! Where are you going?

Howard enters. Carol picks herself up.

CAROL   He stole the box, he's getting away!

HOWARD   What box?

BRENDA   *off stage*   Margery! Quick. Oh God, her face. Howard!

Howard rushes out.

HOWARD   *off stage*   What's she done?

BRENDA   *off*   Look at her face!

CAROL   *running out*   Jay! Jay did it. He's got our money.

HOWARD   *off*   He's gone upstairs. Get him.

BRENDA *off* Will she be alright?

CAROL *off* Get Jay! Get Jay!

Terry is utterly alone now, listening to the chase.

HOWARD *off* Jay! Get down here!

Carol *off* He's there, look, he's getting out the landing window!

HOWARD *off* Jay, get down!

CAROL *off* Will she die? She won't die will she? Liz?

BRENDA *off* I hope you fall!

CAROL *off* Come on, let's go outside and get him!

BRENDA *off* Fall!

HOWARD *off* Shut up! Get back upstairs!

BRENDA *off* Come on.

HOWARD *off* Stay in the house! I'll get him, Liz.

More running. Their voices now come from the garden.

TERRY I didn't tell them, Jay! I kept my promise! I never said anything!

BRENDA *off* He's there, look. Come on, fall!

TERRY I never told, Jay! You're my friend, I never told.

VOICES *off, chanting* Fall! Fall! Fall *chanting continues*

HOWARD *off* Get into the house! Get into the house! Mind out of the way. Jay, don't move. Don't try to move!

TERRY *above the chanting* He's not to fall! He's my friend! He's my bestest friend! Don't tell him to fall!

The chanting subsides.

LIZ *off* It's alright, Margery, you'll be alright. They're on their way, my love, they'll be here in a minute.

HOWARD *off* Jay, stay still, don't try to move. I'll get the ladder. We're getting the – Jay!

BRENDA *off* He's going to fall!

HOWARD *off* Jay!

Screams.

71

TERRY   NO! NOOOOOO!

He collapses, curling up to try to keep it all out. the screams stop suddenly. The only sound is **Terry**'*s repeated, agonizing 'no'.*

CAROL   *off*   Is he dead?

HOWARD   *off*   Go in, all of you, go in.

CAROL   *off*   I think he's dead.

HOWARD   *off*   Please. Go in, all of you.

Pause.

TERRY   I never told them, Jay, I never said anything.

He is rocking, sobbing.

TERRY   I kept my promise. You're my friend. I never said anything.

He is shocked, he rocks and begins to sing to himself, softly. It is a Christmas carol.

Staging the Play

Handle with Care has no stars. All the characters are important and the success of the play will demand that everyone works together to create a convincing group of people and the tense, claustrophobic atmosphere of the house in which they live.

Try to understand more about the character you are playing by building up a life story for them. Some of the characters give us clues about their background, others are more vague. Make a list of the facts you *know* about them from the play – age, fragments of past history, likes and dislikes, personal qualities, their fantasy lives, what they need most. What else will you have to discover or invent about your character before you can get on the inside of your part? Use some of the ideas in the later sections of this book to get to know your character better, or make up some scenes of your own. What is your character up to when he is not in front of the audience? Think of what is happening offstage.

Remember, an audience learns about the characters in a play from *everything* they see on stage, not just from the words which are spoken. Characters reveal their feelings by what they do or do not do, by what they say or do not say, and particularly in the way they react to one another. Barry, for instance, has very few lines in the play, but he is often on stage and his silent presence may be made very important to the audience.

THE SET

There is only one main acting area in the play – the living room. Everything else can be suggested. The boys' bedroom can be represented by setting aside part of the acting area, and using a few simple props. It would be possible to stage this play 'in the round' and indicate the shape of the room with the furniture used, though this may present problems for the actors. Work out the acting area and organise the furniture early on, so that actors can begin to feel comfortable as they rehearse.

Lighting will be important. Try to have a suggestion of sunlight streaming in from the garden, and moonlight in Scene 8. The bedroom is always shown in darkness, the candle in the seance just showing up faces. A small lamp, especially one which lights the faces from underneath, could be very effective.

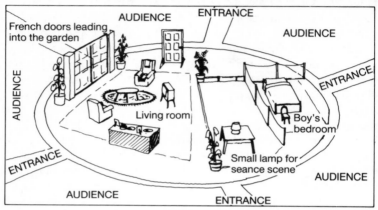

MUSIC

Music can help create atmosphere, in the same way background music does in a film, but take care that it does not drown the actors' voices or intrude at the wrong time. Encourage your music teacher to get a group of musicians together who can experiment with sound – in particular with synthesisers – to get the effect you want. You can always put the music on tape if you don't want live musicians. An alternative is to use extracts from carefully selected recorded tapes. Here are some points in the play where music might help:

1 When Margery's mother leaves: a simple, sad refrain, not too sentimental.
2 The seance: eerie, tense music to help build the scene to a climax.
3 When Margery realises Terry is about to assault her: music to act as a 'signal' for what is to come. Aim for a menacing quality, to build the tension.
4 Between scenes: music that helps to create the mood.

Background

In 1985 there were 97 000 children and young people in care. Of these, 42 000 were with foster parents, 37 000 in residential accommodation and 18 000 (mainly adolescents) legally in care but living at home or with a relative or friend.

Residential accommodation is defined as centres providing full-time education; centres with remand, observation and assessment facilities; centres with hostel accommodation; residential nurseries (for the under-sevens); centres without specialist functions. It is the last three of these that we refer to as children's homes.

Why are young people put into children's homes?

If we look at the table, which relates to 234 young people (aged 18 months to 19 years) in a total of twenty homes, we see a variety of reasons. We must not assume that one reason alone puts them there, generally there are several factors involved. In the table we are given 'primary' and 'secondary' reasons.

Reason for child being placed in a home	Primary reason %	Secondary reason %
Neglect or injury	44	10
Behaviour problems at home	32	12
Marital breakdown or problems	29	19
Mental illness of parent(s)	24	9
Homelessness (ie thrown out or refusing to go home)	18	3
Non-school attendance	15	8
Parent(s) in prison	12	3
Financial problems	11	25
Delinquency	11	8
Physical illness of parent(s)	9	6
Behaviour problems at school	8	6
Family homeless	3	1
Confinement of mother	2	1

Reducing people to numbers and categories somehow makes them less real. The researcher who compiled the table noted:

Several cases involving ill treatment were particularly distressing. It is shocking to be told and shown by a child exactly how cigarette burns and scars came to be inflicted. Some children had experienced almost prolonged torture. One girl had been admitted to care at the age of ten with a broken nose, weighing only 29lb, another was discovered when she was seven, grossly neglected, still wearing nappies and able to speak only three words.

This description makes the children into suffering human beings and not just statistics.

Neglect and ill treatment are the main reasons why young people are put into care. A great many, though, do have caring parents who, because of illness, poor housing, unemployment or other problems, have a difficult struggle trying to bring up a family. When they can't cope they may eventually have to put their children into care. Some parents are more willing to do this than others.

Some parents have no choice but to put their children in care, because of poor housing and lack of money.

Who provides children's homes?

1 The local authorities, who receive funding from the public. The Social Services department have responsibility for their management.
2 Voluntary child care bodies such as Dr Barnardo's, national children's homes, The Children's Society. Local authorities sometimes combine with voluntary organisations in the management of homes.
3 Private homes run by individuals on an independent basis, receiving referrals and payments from the local authority.

What are children's homes like?

Who knows, perhaps one day your children or your children's children could be in the same position as me – in a children's home. It's not too bad. We are not locked up and we don't have bread and water to eat and drink every day, though some people think it's like that. Well, I hope you believe me because it isn't like that at all. I wanted to be in care because I could not get on with my stepfather, and he kept hitting me. So I just kept running away from it all. When I went into care it was like my life starting all over again. It was like a holiday. I started going out and meeting people, and eventually started work when I left school. People in this children's home are looked after well, better than living with parents who don't care about you at all.

Girl, aged 15

A children's home at the beginning of the century.

The image of a children's home to a lot of people is of an old-fashioned orphanage, a large gloomy Victorian building in its own grounds with steps leading up to the immense front door and, inside . . . disinfectant, dormitories and a dutiful matron. Fortunately, the buildings themselves and the way they are run have changed greatly. They are brighter, cosier places, more a part of the local community, with more staff and more expertise in dealing with young people. There are some specialist homes, geared to coping with particular ages and problems. Young children, for instance, are generally catered for in a small 'family group' type of home – similar to the real family that they need. Older children are more likely to be in larger 'adolescent hostels', which usually have one person in overall charge, more staff and several specialists. It is an environment which allows young people more of a say in how their own lives are organised.

What does it feel like to be 'in care'?

For someone outside it is a lonely and insecure experience to enter a children's home; one which the children, when they first arrive, must strive to master.

Researcher

Are you my new daddy?
Boy, awaiting a foster placement, to researcher

One of my social workers told me once that somebody had said that being in care had the same effect on you emotionally, like, as having a major operation. I told her that at least if they chopped the wrong leg off you could get compensation and a pension for the rest of your life.

Boy, aged 15

Loneliness and insecurity are just two of the things that someone in care has to try to cope with. These are greatly increased by the frequent moves between homes and between foster parents. Nothing seems to last. Strong bonds with friends and adults are very difficult to achieve.

Trevor is seventeen now. His life in care began when he was a year old. He has not seen his parents since. He was fostered for five months, then for six weeks, then placed in a children's home for two years, then with foster parents for seven years, taken away and put in an observation and assessment centre for his behaviour problems, and finally he spent three years in a children's home. When asked how many people have looked after him during his life he smiles wryly and answers, "Dozens and none."

Level of contact between children and natural parents	Proportion of children %
Weekly	41
Monthly	16
Occasionally	23
No contact	20

(Source: David Berridge *Children's Homes, Basil Blackwell, 1985*)

The table gives the number of visits that young people in care receive. It is based on a study of 234 children in 20 homes and shows that two in every five children in care are in weekly contact with their families, but one child in five has no contact.

DRAMA

1 Splitting the family

Organisation	Work in a group of four or five. One of you is a social worker, the others are members of the same family.
Situation	Because of illness or housing problems the family has to split up. How will the social worker convince them that they must be split up for their own good? If the family becomes violent, will the police be called?
Opening line	Social Worker: We're only trying to help you.

Inside a modern home for teenagers.

WRITING

1 Imagine that you are either the social worker or one of the family in the drama *Splitting the family*, on the previous page. Write a letter to a friend about the incident.
2 As a new inmate to a children's home, write a diary entry for the first day you spent there. How does the place appear to you, and what kind of impression have the other people there made on you? Is it possible that you might be *glad* to be in the home? If so, explain in your diary why you are relieved or happy.
3 As a young child in a home, write a letter to Father Christmas. What would you be most likely to want for Christmas?
4 Imagine that you have recently arrived in a children's home. You have one relation who might be able to take you in. Write a letter to this person, explaining what life in the home is like. Will they offer to take you into their family?

FURTHER ACTIVITIES

1 Try to find out about the range of work that the voluntary child-care bodies are involved in. When you see exactly what they do and what they hope to do in the future, you might like to help them raise funds.
2 Find out about the children's homes in your area. They may not be called children's homes but residential centres, community homes, etc. How many are there? If there is one close to you perhaps you could arrange a visit and talk to the house-parents (if they can spare some time) about their work.

Fostering

Fostering, where children are accepted into families and brought up by them, but without being adopted, has been recognised as a good way of caring for children rather than placing them in institutions. Obviously it is much more successful with younger children. Older children are more likely to be un-responsive and suspicious of their new family. For some of them, fostering may not be the answer. Unfortunately, there are not enough willing foster parents to go round, in spite of regular appeals for new foster parents in newspapers, on radio and television.

A fifteen-year-old girl in care described what happened to her during an unsuccessful fostering appeal:

> Me and them other kids, we stood there all day in that department store with two social workers from nine in the morning till gone four in the afternoon. I felt like I was in a cattle market, you know? A lot of people came up and asked our names, gave us sweets and the rest – a bit like being in a zoo, really. But all of them hundreds of people shopping there that Saturday, none of them wanted me to live with them, did they? I've thought about that a lot since.

DRAMA

1 Looking for a home

Organisation   Work with a group of three or four. One of you is a reporter from the local radio or TV. The others are children in care who are looking for foster parents, and perhaps one of the group might be a social worker.

Situation   The reporter is writing a news item about fostering children. How will the children respond to questions?

Opening line   Reporter: How long have you been standing here?

2 Persuasion

Organisation   Work in a small group. You are all members of the same family, both adults and younger people.

Situation   One of you has been in the department store, and has spoken to one of the children there. You feel that your family should offer to foster this child. How can you persuade the rest of the family that this is the right thing to do?

Family Member: If only you'd seen them standing there. . . .

3 The Visit

Organisation Work with a group of three or four. One of you is a child in care who is looking for foster parents. The others are a couple or a family who would like to foster a child.

Situation You have been invited to spend the weekend with the family in their own home. How might the visit turn out?

Opening line Adult: We hope you'll be happy here.

Development If it seems appropriate, show your scene to the rest of the class. Try to select two or three moments which will show clearly whether the visit is likely to be a success.

Social workers counsel teenagers in care and explain the different options available to them at each stage.

Work on and Around the Script

DRAMA

1 Neighbours

Organisation   Work in a group of three or four. Imagine that you are adults who live in the same street or even next door to *Sunflowers*.

Situation   You are aware of some of the events that have been taking place and are worried or disturbed by them. Each of you can choose to be either sympathetic towards the young people or critical of everything to do with the home.

Opening line   Neighbour: I don't know what's going on in there.

2 A visit from the doctor

Organisation   The script mentions that Brenda, who thinks she has seen a ghost, has had a visit from the doctor. Work with one or two friends. One of you is the doctor and one is Brenda. The third will be Liz or Howard.

Situation   The doctor has discovered that there is nothing physically wrong with Brenda, and is trying to find out why she is so upset. Will she say what she has seen?

Opening line   Doctor: Now, Brenda, I want you to tell me why you haven't been sleeping properly.

3 Breaking the news

Organisation   Work with a partner. One of you is Margery, and the other is Margery's mother.

Situation   It is before the play begins. Margery's mother has decided that she is going to put Margery in a home. Now she has to break the news to her daughter.

Opening line   Mother: I just can't cope any more.

4 Job satisfaction

Organisation   It is clear from the play that Liz and Howard have jobs which are responsible and demanding. Work with a partner. One of you is either Liz or Howard. The other is a friend who is thinking of going into the same profession.

Situation   Your friend has come to you for advice. Would you encourage them to take up the same kind of work? What qualities will they need to be successful? What advice would you give them?

Opening line   Friend: It must be a wonderful feeling to be able to help young people.

Development   Try this scene twice – once before things start to go wrong at Sunflowers, and then after the events of the play. Would the conversation remain the same?

5 Investigations

Organisation   Work in a group of four or five. One or two of you imagine that you are Liz and Howard. The others are officials from the Social Services.

Situation   An inquiry is being held into the recent events at Sunflowers. What questions will Liz and Howard have to answer? How will they explain what happened? Will they take the blame?

Opening line   Social Services Official: This is a very serious matter.

6 The Media

Organisation   Work in a group of three or four. One of you is a TV newsreader, the others are reporters, local people, teachers, social services workers, etc.

Situation	Create an item for the local television news about what has been happening in Sunflowers. Include interviews with people who may have been involved or who have opinions about the case.
Opening line	Newsreader: Two days ago, a boy from Sunflowers. . . .

7 Scenes from a life

Organisation	Work in a small group. One of you is Jay, and the others in the group are different characters from his life.
Situation	Create three or four brief scenes from Jay's early life, which will show how his experience has turned him into the kind of person we see in the play. You might include moments which will show him as a young child, in school, or in his original family.

8 Meaning

Organisation	Work with a partner. One of you is one of the adults or children who was at Sunflowers during the events of the play. The other is a friend.
Situation	At least ten years have passed since the events in the play. Your friend is asking you about your past. What will you say? How do these events appear to you now that you are older and so many years have passed?
Opening line	I don't think I'll ever forget. . . .

WRITING

1 Read the poem Autobiography carefully. What do you think has happened to the child in the poem to bring 'the black dreams'? Is this the kind of poem that one of the characters in the play might have written? (You could discuss these points with the class or in groups.) Now choose one of the young people in the play and write a short poem as if you were that person.

Autobiography

In my childhood trees were green
And there was plenty to be seen.
   Come back early or never come.

My father made the walls resound,
He wore his collar the wrong way round.
   Come back early or never come.

My mother wore a yellow dress;
Gently, gently, gentleness.
   Come back early or never come.

When I was five the black dreams came;
Nothing after was quite the same.
   Come back early or never come.

The dark was talking to the dead;
The lamp was dark beside my bed.
   Come back early or never come.

When I woke they did not care;
Nobody, nobody was there.
   Come back early or never come.

When my silent terror cried,
Nobody, nobody replied.
   Come back early or never come.

I got up; the chilly sun
Saw me walk away alone.
   Come back early or never come.

Louis Macneice

2   Create a file on one of the young people in the play – the kind of file which the Social Services might have. Include details of their family life, based on what you have picked up from the play. Include any recommendations you may have about their future – such as fostering, adoption, returning to their family, going to an adolescent hostel. Finish with a note written when the character is 21 years old. What has happened to them?

Bruce Oldfield, the dress designer, was brought up in a Dr Barnardo's home.

3   There are several lines and incidents in the play that show how Terry is desperate for friendship. Look carefully at these and see what they reveal about Terry's attitude to friendship – for instance, what qualities does he expect a friend to have, how does he judge friendship and respond to it. Now imagine that you are Terry and write a short description entitled "My ideal friend".

4   Be yourself now, and write a brief account of the friendship you enjoy with one or two of your best friends. What do you like about each other, how do you show your friendship, what interests and activities do you share, and so on. Then compare your personal account with 'Terry's' description in question 3. In what ways are they different; in what ways are they the same?

The Supernatural

Strange visitors

A belief in ghosts is a common feature of supernatural philosophy. The explanation given is that very occasionally when a person dies – traditionally, in tragic or mysterious circumstances – the spirit becomes 'trapped' and unable to leave the material world. This spirit or 'ghost' then remains to haunt the scene of the tragedy. Ghosts are usually seen (by those who believe in them) as a shadowy outline of a person or thing.

Poltergeists, on the other hand, are spirits which are heard but not seen. There are very many reports of their hyperactive behaviour. Sometimes objects, such as crockery, furniture and stones are thrown about. Poltergeists have been blamed for starting rain and fires, and have been said to assault people with blows and scratches. Whatever the cause of such happenings, poltergeist activity does seem to have one common factor: disturbances are often linked with the presence of a young person. Why is this? Might it be because they have vivid imaginations and a sense of mischief?

DRAMA

1   *A poltergeist?*

Organisation   Work in a small group. You are the characters in the play, or other young people in a similar situation.

Situation   It is later in the same day on which a mess has been created in the store cupboard. Something else has happened – crockery has been smashed, a picture has fallen down, furniture has moved unexpectedly. How do you all react? Do you try to find a rational explanation.

Opening line   Howard: Something is going on in here.

2   Ghost stories

Organisation   Work with a partner. One of you is a young person, the other is an elderly relation in whose house you are staying.

Situation   After watching a rather creepy play on TV one evening, the elderly person starts to talk about how the house you are staying in was once supposed to be haunted.

Opening line   Elderly Relative: I've never actually seen or heard anything strange myself, mind, but. . . .

Borley Rectory, Essex, was thought to be the most haunted house in Britain, until it was destroyed by fire.

The Runaways

A man is walking home late at night. He has a strange, uneasy feeling. As he gets closer he begins to hear a rumbling and realises that it is coming from inside his own house. Instinctively he knows it to be something abnormal, inexplicable. He waits . . .

90

Then suddenly, ashamed of my cowardice, I seized my bunch of keys, picked out the one I wanted, thrust it into the lock, turned it twice, and pushing the door with all my force hurled it back against the wall inside.

The bang echoed like a gunshot and immediately the crash was answered by a terrific uproar from cellar to attic. I could now distinguish an extraordinary sound of trampling on the stairs, parquet floors and carpets, a trampling not of human feet or shoes but of crutches, wooden crutches and iron crutches, that rang with the metallic insistence of cymbals. Suddenly, on the threshold of the front door, I saw an armchair, my big reading chair, come waddling out; it moved off down the drive. It was followed by others from the drawing room; next came the sofas, low on the ground and crawling along like crocodiles on their stumpy legs, then all the rest of my chairs, leaping like goats, and the little stools loping along like rabbits. . . .

I saw my writing desk appear, a rare eighteenth century collector's piece, containing all my letters, the whole record of anguished passion long since spent. And in it were also my photographs.

Suddenly all fear left me; I threw myself upon it and grappled with it, as one grapples with a burglar; but it went on its way irresistibly, and, in spite of my utmost efforts, I could now even slow it up. As I wrestled like a madman against this terrible strength, I fell to the ground in the struggle. It rolled me over and over and dragged me along the gravel, and already the pieces of furniture behind were beginning to tread on me, trampling and bruising my legs; then, when I let go, the others swept over me, like a cavalry charge over an unhorsed soldier.

At last, mad with terror, I managed to drag myself off the main drive and hide amongst the trees. . . .

From the short story 'Who Knows' *by Guy De Maupassant in Prisoners of War and Other Stories (New Windmill Series)*

3   The Runaways

Organisation	Work with a partner. Read the extract carefully. One of you is the person who watched their furniture run away. The other is a policeman.
Situation	You have gone to the police station to report the loss of your furniture. What evidence have you for what has happened? How will you convince people of the truth of what you say?
Opening line	Owner: My furniture just walked out on me.

DISCUSSION

1 Do you believe in ghosts? Some people have had supernatural experiences. Share your ideas with your friends.
2 If there are such things as ghosts, poltergeists and other supernatural manifestations, what are they? Why do they come back? Is it revenge, something left unfinished, to deliver a message or put things right?

WRITING

Family's horror

A family claims that its home has been invaded by demons which have attacked them.

Mrs Janet Smurl (39) of West Pittston, Pennsylvania, said that for 18 months she and her husband Jack, their four daughters and Mr Smurl's parents have shared their home of 14 years with what they believe is a demonic horde.

Family members claim they have been dragged from bed, slapped and viciously scratched by unseen hands, and that the family's Alsatian dog has been beaten and slammed against walls.

Psychic happenings are frequently reported in the media.

1 Create a newspaper headline about some psychic happening. Then write the newspaper report, in which you expose the event as a hoax or a fraud.
2 Write your own ghost stories. Here are some ideas, but use one of your own if you prefer.

● A group of young people are talking about ghosts late at night. They are having fun scaring one another. Someone decides to play a trick, perhaps dressing up as a ghost. Maybe the false ghost meets a real ghost; or someone else who knows about the trick thinks he is talking to the false ghost but in fact it turns out to be. . . .

● A traveller needs a place to stay late at night. He finds a pleasant house where the host is very friendly. Next morning he discovers that the host is a ghost!